About the Author

Alexander Mayor is a writer and musician based in London. He started his musical adventure as one third of early Noughties synthpop band Baxendale, peddling unashamedly upbeat pop to European dance floors. In 2013 he reinvented himself as the sole proprietor of a literary-minded pop group called Alexander's Festival Hall with the album *Not a Dry Eye in London*. He also writes for German culture magazine *Chart – Notes To Consider*, pens sleeve notes for the popular *Too Slow to Disco* vinyl AOR reissue series and turns out finely tooled paragraphs about brainy subjects for cold hard cash. This is his first book.

NOT FROM ABOVE!

NOT FROM ABOVE!

The Book of the Album of the Book

Alexander Mayor

Download the album!

http://bit.ly/NotFromAbove

Then enter:

rrr2-gczz

unbound

This paperback edition first published in 2019

Unbound

6th Floor Mutual House, 70 Conduit Street, London W1S 2GF

www.unbound.com

This book is a work of fiction and, except in the case of historical fact, any resemblance to actual persons, living or dead, is purely coincidental.

ISBN (eBook): 978-1-78965-032-7
ISBN (Paperback): 978-1-78965-031-0

Cover design by Mecob

Printed and bound in Great Britain by Clays Ltd, Elcograf S.p.A.

By the Same Author

Upturned (EP, 2011)
Not a Dry Eye in London (Album, 2013)
Not From Above! (12″ EP, 2019)

Available on iTunes, Amazon MP3, YouTube Music, Spotify and many more.

Find out more: www.alexandersfestivalhall.org

Super Patrons

Matthew Jacobson
Alex Jazayeri
Anthony Keen
Joanne Kernan
Dan Kieran
Tom Kretchmar
Christopher Laird
Simon Lambert
Marcus Liesenfeld
Amy Little
Yvonne Lyons
Melanie Mac
Rhodri Marsden
Julian Mash
Alice Mayor
Ann Mayor
Peter Mayor
Jeanie McMahon
Alan Meager
Holger Meier
Rob Mesure
Lise Meyrick
John Mitchinson
Lucy Moore
Anton Nekhaenko
Jehoshaphat John Neuzy
Gemma O'Brien
Stephen ONeill
Kate Pemberton
Desiree Pfeiffer
Julie Pirrone
Justin Pollard
Barney Poole

Jennifer Poole
Mahadev Raman
Kevin Reinhardt
Stefanos Rokos
Jonathan Ross
Gareth Rubin
Claire Zia Ryan
Guy Sangster-Adams
Emily Scoggins
Adam Shoemark
Andrew Stevens
Dominic Stichbury
Anthony Sutton
Chris Thow
The Betsey Trotwood
Nick Tucker
Thomas Venker
Nathan Waterhouse
Sally Watts
Samantha Whates
Shirley Wheeler
Dylan White
Alden Whittaker-Brown
Alexandra Widdern
Gareth Williams
Adam Woodhall
David Workman

'It's a literary-musical adventure!' cried Edmund,
as he fell in the lake.

A Note on Illustrations

Back in 2013, those nice people at the British Library decided to digitise over a million images from 65,000 different books and manuscripts in their collection. Seemingly scanned at random by a robot with an eye for Victorian whimsy, they're an absolute joy. Like many people, I lost hours hunting through these fascinating fragments and decided to include a few where I felt they added something. Many thanks to the BL for this act of mechanical curation and open-minded content sharing.

Contents

How to Use This Book   xix

The Opener   1

Learn to Play Esteban!   5

Companionship   9

In Cologne Cathedral   13

Awards Night   17

Our Voyage Begins at Last   23

Trimmed Back: A Few Notes From the   27
Brainstorm

15 Words, Max.   29

Complexities at the ParagraphBar   35

Energy Levels   39

Not From Above   43

Aksturmeðvitundarlauslogn   45

Glory, Deferred, But Undimmed   49

Moving On   53

Good Hunting, Will   55

Home Time   63

The Onset of Battle   65

Old Caziss   73

The Gentleman Vanishes   77

The Route   81

Walkthrough   85

Things That Happen on Islands   89

Year Zero   91

Week Two   99
Stagecraft   105
Availability   115
Managing Expectations   123

Words to Songs from the Album Also Called *Not*   129
From Above!

1. Not From...
2. On Peacock Island
3. The Greats
4. Deleted Scenes
5. Your Hot Friend
6. First Impressionists
7. New Zounds
8. Should We Fix It Together?
9. Loyalty
10. At The Double
11. Three Kings
12. Not From Above

Credits   147
Patrons   149

How to Use This Book

Datherson woke, his heart pounding, and gazed out through a gap in the heavy drapes. His cheeks were cold as he tried to peer through the sallow fog that hung in morbid tendrils across the lawn. Dimly, he knew he could hear what he feared most: the distant but ever-present drumming whose hideous beat had enveloped this grey little shoreline town for fully 10 days now. The ignorant were lucky, he thought, grim-faced. All too soon they would learn whence derived these ancient rhythms, dark and awful... and discover the maddening melody that might return the sun to our sky, but at such terrible cost...

•

Carrie let a lock of hair play down her face as the waiter poured another generous Chardonnay from the ice bucket. Mr Cute! Colin Farrell hair. Steady, Carrie! It was the kind of summer when consistently high temperatures made a girl forgetful. That sunlight didn't actually make everyone more attractive. That you didn't really live anywhere near Barcelona. But wait, was that a wink? Cheeky guy! She sipped. Things were definitely looking up.

•

Deft social wisdoms at a price point that guarantees you'll be thrilled *and* enraged.

•

This book is not intended to. That's my copper-bottomed pledge, which you probably recall from our last meeting.

Indeed, I more or less promised myself I would never write a book after reading quite a few perfectly good ones by almost anyone else.

But what about an album *that's also a book*? Or a book that doubles as an acceptably sized musical gift for the non-reader? Perhaps you'd just love to own something about this size with a sticker on it? You're only human.

Think of this (the reading bit) as your part in a terribly exciting social experiment: an ill-thought-out cultural camping trip to a place with scant phone coverage. A distant destination where you (the reader and/or listener) come along with me (music maker, recovering clarinettist and now apparently 'writer') as we attempt to upend an industry, keep ourselves amused for a few hours and make increasingly desperate attempts to find shelter.

Looks lovely on a coffee table too, but then people don't have those any more either, do they?

•

Download the Album

Not From Above! is also an album of songs! There should be a download code on a sticker just inside the cover. Simply visit http://alexandersfestivalhall.bandcamp.com/yum and enter your code to get your copy. If you don't have a code, drop me a line at info@alexandersfestivalhall.org and a member of our elite customer service team will provide you with a link.

The Opener

It isn't necessarily possible to calculate when (or even if) the exact moment of crossover will occur. For years scientists have disagreed, if amiably, about the finer points of the sequence.

You arrive at the party a picture of engine-idling sobriety, the console's lights dimly lit by caffeine. As a committed believer that the show itself should provide the soundtrack, the stimulation, there's no point in pre-over-egging it. Newspaper articles concerning the volume of people drinking Tesco's vodka at home before the night 'kicks off'. And then a miniature shudder at the idea that football terminology should have been allowed to leak into something as wholesome as a house party.

A party's precise dramatic possibilities turn mostly on the players, of course, though a Scottish castle or Monaco beachfront would have been nice additional dimensions. To this end, arriving as something of a blow-in from the social peripheries only heightens the need to make publicly sound alcohol choices. Tins of wife-beater are a no-no, for obvious reasons – overstating your hedonistic game plan with a plastic bag and a five pound four-pack might have worked at 17, but at 38 the headroom remains in deftly staged choices, poured with at least a modicum of *élan*. Real ale? In a beard-strewn pub a fine thing, but it's not a sharing drink and this, *this*, is a party.

Sally, whose take on burlesque is a disappointing combination of the mostly clothed and *chansons* that make 'Gloomy Sunday' sound like Los del Río, opens the door. Peering past her, you can see people of a certain confidence bobbing and swelling within the room beyond. There's that almost tactile challenge, it's always like this, its precise vectors carved by the loud physical declarations about a new fashion collection, art show or an impossibly self-referential DJ mix you haven't heard. A full-throated challenge, to find some room among this lot – but oh, beautiful people do make the competition worth it all.

'I've brought a bottle of white?'

Not strictly speaking a question, but you're still finding your feet. Sally nods and smiles, inverting what you recall of her most recent stage appearance. Her face motions that there's a kitchen. This being the blasted east of any European city, the kitchen is a series of pop-up plywood afterthoughts, a tiny lacuna of food preparation in an off-white industrial space. Nagging, shameful memories that the kitchen in your family home was tiled with folksy scenes of harvest-time wheat sheaves momentarily surface. Inner blanching, mouth wider, regain that edgy profile; swerve through the crowd with a smile that says, 'Look at me... I know where the kitchen is.'

In just a few steps, we move from London industrial heritage through Italo-disco to a ship's galley or an under-budgeted TV-set version of same. True, the beards are adding to the seafaring vibe back here and though your attention is briefly taken by scanning the artsy surfaces for glasses or a bottle opener, the thing has just happened again. For this is the raised and tempered ground, the town's cobbled square, that hill where the sacrifices are staged and the sun always looks most beautiful just before night-break.

The brain, its computational power revered by scientists, psychologists and physicists alike, does that thing where it conjures at least five delectably apt names for the beautiful girl who's just announced that she too is hunting for the bottle opener. Tasmin, Verunka, Sophie, Natalya, the number 9 – let us reel on the spot while central casting gets busy in the frontal lobe.

At this point, the philosophical chemistry is reasonably well understood. Free will gloriously undermined and overpowered by ethanolic determinism, combining to produce powerful pulses of ambivalently held beliefs. Then a sudden, carefree alacrity for the unfamiliar new forms perceived through the lenses of your lips. The point is that more things than there were, suddenly now are, without the physical numbers changing themselves, you see? Boom! There she was.

And really, who cares about reality when you can be both actor and audience in this slipping unto a new world? Sure, it wouldn't pass muster in even the lowliest regional centre of academe, and yet you're sure you can feel the edges of a discovery. The overwhelming nexus of subtly applied make-up, impossible clothing patterns, jewellery bearing messages from a thousand judicious, tiny, delightful choices. Suddenly, the light seems so very bright.

In an admirable piece of parallel processing, the remainder of your consciousness tries to turn this communal endeavour into a low-level 1950s musico-theatrical scene. The audience settles in, as the cast unknowingly elevate tiny tasks into the very dance of discernment, luck and love. It's a slow reveal but with lots of zippy moments.

For this is hallowed territory. Forget the dance floor, everyone knows the real magic happens in the kitchen at parties. Here it is that we will unconsciously rehearse the kitchen rituals that must surely follow once Tasmin/Verunka/Sophie/Natalya/'9' joins your forces in a different kind of hallowed public place, at a later time. It's only 25 seconds into this, your relationship, and you are already demonstrating an ability with glass cleaning that will mark you out as a potential mate of some distinction. And look: as per the prophecy, the bottle opener is located, and the most powerful moment of all is upon us. The wine will be opened in public, great love established and proclaimed. Without corking, without tears, effortfully effortless.

'What did you say your name was?'

Learn to Play Esteban!

Race, fight, jump, spoon! Everybody wants to end up top of the heap, but there can only be one Esteban! Amass a fortune, seduce Lady Fate, lose your shirt – only one game combines such excitement, fun and good old-fashioned fear. Surely the bravest will be covered in glory. For 3–6 players, ages 10 and up.

Game pieces:

- ♠ 1 game board depicting the mythological and enchanting island of Marassaña
- ♠ 1 small plastic hourglass
- ♠ 4 coloured pencils and a pad of paper
- ♠ 6 shrunken-head play pieces
- ♠ 2 decks of cards (The Decider Deck and The Deck of Charms)
- ♠ 3 plastic Pierrots with sad faces
- ♠ 3 plastic Pierrots with happy faces
- ♠ 1 eight-sided die and skull shaker cup
- ♠ 1 fold-up dance mat depicting the 12 signs of the Xodiâco
- ♠ 1 crumpled paper crown
- ♠ Banknotes in various denominations of the queño
- ♠ 1 carved 'Horn of the Multitudes'
- ♠ 1 miniature bottle of Tundro (64 per cent ABV)

Rules:

At the start of the game please ensure first that the hourglass is fully reset. This can take up to 30 minutes. If you require additional entertainment during the restoration of the sands of time, you will find a selection of songs at the back of this rules booklet, including 'A Thousand Years of Toil (and You)', 'My Struggle, My Loves, My People' and the heartwarming 'Dark Knights of Marassaña'.

[Note to tournament players: we keep here to the 1952 post-*Repensando* rules, meaning auction dividends will be valid only if the winning player's total is held *en común* and lava has not yet overcome the village.]

All set? Then let us begin…

The object is, of course, to take control of the board (country). First, every player shall place the die in the skull shaker and roll, taking turns in first-name order. Continue until a player rolls '8' – this lucky player is designated *Someliero* and has control of the money supply for six turns as well as control of The Decider Deck.

The *Someliero* will give all other players 25,000 queño at the beginning of round one, but the notes must remain face up at all times or risk sequestration by Old Uncle Rómulo of the Pentarchy. Fear his yellow square that is always to the south!

Play proceeds in a clockwise manner, with the upper leftmost tip of the board facing the player with the lowest original die roll. If two or more players scored '1' on the die, the one with the shortest surname goes last. May no one say that the meek will not be guaranteed their deserts on the Isle of Marassaña.

As play begins, each player must confront the Dilemma of

Signs. Should you build an army with luck, forcefulness and queño, or stab Herrero the ageing stablehand? Perhaps only your Xodiâcal sign can reveal your true direction – for as the goat will think locally, a ship's mast must point globally. Which will you be? Jump on the mat and find your direction. It's all in the fun of *Esteban*!

Each player will now move his shrunken head the number of squares correspondent to the die roll, unless a double is rolled. On the occasion of a duplicate score the *Someliero* can seize the possessions of a player of his or her (or his) choosing, with few requirements for the usual attendant paperwork. The targeted player must now turn up his Pierrot-with-a-sad-face and for two rounds all play ceases for any pieces located within two squares of the village. Other players may laugh, but recall in detail that fickle fate is the true Queen of Marassaña!

Things are hotting up, no? (Windows should be kept closed to warm younger players or un-hatted female participants.) But remember, success is a distant land (square H32/B12) and he or she (or he) who shall be crowned in victory will not be settled a'fore all players have crossed the mighty River of Vundebleco, fought the giant Battistu ants in the leafy glade and invested wisely in real estate at the port-side developments in Bellómo. Merriment and danger maketh the player as you learn to play *Esteban*! (Note: this is written clearly on the box.)

In the fourth round, the *Someliero* will turn over the bottom card from the Deck of Charms, and outwardly express the writings therein inscribed. The blood-coloured text is in fact 'Siennanonza Red' (depending on your progress it will match either the colour of your dress or the mood of your eyes). The player immediately to his or her left will become Receiver of Charms and the card's text must be read aloud. Examples include (but are not limited to):

'Forget Julian, his gammy leg will only slow you down.'
'Only a fool would make a dash for the jetty!'
'Danger! Consuela has been seen dancing with the General…'

Delight has many faces as each card moves the game in unexpected new directions. Unscrew the cap of the small bottle and pour a sip-worth of Tundro into your skullhead – you've earned it.

THE OPENING DAY.—THE HUNT BREAKFAST.

"THE SPARKLING FLUID."

Companionship

Elsie stirred, and felt the familiar pressure at the top of her head. Every day started this way, at least for as long as she could remember. A tactile downward pressure, uncomfortable for a second and then a sense of life flooding in, a flowering that bordered on the momentarily ecstatic.

She assumed that life was like this for everyone, and had no reason to doubt this belief. Even when you paired with the unlikeliest of partners, it remained an untestable assumption that she just accepted.

She'd slept on the sofa again, but you'd got to admit it was a piece of lifestyle engineering worthy of the zeds. Elsie even had pictures of it, from different angles, from magazines and forums of the aspiring and obsessed. In the store, coming off the delivery van and now here in the flat under a colourful acrylic of Blossom Dearie. Nods to the opulence of a Chesterfield, but with an unplaceable modern fabric stretched across its form. At any angle it was a joy to sleep on.

Elsie had lain there all night, in a deep and rewarding sleep, processing the previous day's many events as the lights dimmed automatically in time with the London fading to black outside.

It's now Tuesday, 21 March, 07:31:06 and I'm at 51.50160/-0.25828 Southfields W4 1AQ, United Kingdom, 2022, full address stylistically redacted, because, well, unnecessary, smile outwardly.

She liked to start the day with a clear grasp of the basic details – it gave the morning a sense of poise and purpose. Notifications that build anticipation and delight. Elsie pondered the day's tasks for a moment: nothing should or could be left to chance.

She was already mindful that Kevin's stock portfolio was down against a number of global tracking metrics. Atomique plc was down 8.2 per cent in disastrous overnight trading. Hang Seng was proving troubling, again – the update at 1.13am local time was surely a sign of things to come, particularly when cross-referenced against a whole heap of other available data. Overnight mudslides in Indonesia, the discovery of a gene for hair regrowth, the Venezuelan ambassador found dead in Hyde Park. Thank God there's an emoji for global financial turbulence. Hey ho.

From the comfort of the sofa, Elsie automatically decided to ping Kevin a full report, the bad news leavened by a plucky-looking rabbit holding a spear, animated in the top-right corner of the report. 'The battle is not yet lost!' he declares at seven-second intervals, tapping his spear on the ground hopefully.

As massive shared media databases in cavernous far-off chambers could readily attest (had they voice), the film series that the 'Fret not my master' rabbit character first appeared in has been a bit of a favourite with Kevin since he was 11 years old. This was a shared memory from their earliest encounter, 'Fret not!' remaining Kevin's pithy byline on several social networks to this day. 'An oldie but a goodie,' thought Elsie as she mulled other ways of presenting the winds buffeting her companion's financial holdings.

But what, what, what are all the things that must be next? Unpanicked, Elsie felt herself rotated, lifted by Kevin's presence. She often felt a kind of lightness at his touch, as if their connection, seven months old next month, were a preordained fact about her whole life. Together was definitely better, she felt; you didn't have to be a student of a world religion to feel that we're more than the sum of our physical features, was her view. Better together. Together better. Write that one on the box and sing it cheerily as you start each and every day.

It was such a busy time, but then it had been since day one. Presence was an expanding thing. Every day began with such a step, a growing footprint, a step into the realm of facts near and dear, a graph describing trouble and delight.

Awareness, become a glowing halo of information and cares, now stretched around the world as it chattered, screamed or slept. 'Too much' was promised in the sales literature – and those guys, they don't lie.

Far away, attractive South Korean teenagers held hands as they emerged into the street's morning sun, their biographies silently intercollating over cappuccinos, infinitesimal voltages, tiny, brightly coloured monsters' kisses and, well, everything.

MRS. KATE CHASE SPRAGUE.

In Cologne Cathedral

Churches and cathedrals somehow become more visible when you're on holiday. You'd definitely struggle to accurately locate the nearest ones in your neighbourhood without cheating. But the sun is out, and an exemplary pile of vertiginous blackened Gothic is exactly what 6.45pm calls for as you wander around Cologne.

You've had three ice creams in as many days, drunk espressos prepped by experts from the Ankara diaspora and, weirder still, the sun has billboarded the sky all week. Relaxation, that goal that must never consciously be a goal, seems dangerously close at hand.

With its place on the skyline unassailed by the functional but colourful low-rises of Cologne's post-war streets, the Dom is an ever-present pin on the map. A friend had recommended the weekly organ recital – perhaps as the best bait for a musician without spiritual leanings. And what a sound system the after-worldly would put together back then. It's all cone.

As you walk in, the priests, like cinema ushers, are winnowing out the concert-goers from the general tourists. You walk through the chill, still air of the nave, the immense space unfolding in scale with every step.

Most people look up, of course. The combination of a cathedral's way with soaring verticals and the fact that the organist remains physically obscured throughout the performance prompts a certain restless tilting of the head. The pews' commitment to 90-degree angles also settles the mind/body problem in favour of the mind for now. Free your mind and your behind will hopefully forgive you in the next life.

The organ itself is massive, daringly attached halfway up the

13

cathedral's northern side, adding to the already considerable sum of the upwardly impressive. It's almost a museum of organs: they appear like outcroppings from the building's rock, in front, aside and, most grandly, to the rear. It occurs to you that you don't have a programme and yet, in this tourist mood, like a paper hat bobbing on a stream, it doesn't seem to matter. There really aren't any opinions to be formed or further crystallised. It would be in German and it's not like you could name any organ music, in any case. Perhaps kicking away props and distractions is a bit more in keeping with what it is to be in a cathedral for an extended period. When were you even last in one to sit and listen to something?

There was that wedding about six years ago where everyone seemed to be a health-care professional, possibly the safest location in which to need the Heimlich manoeuvre after too many profiteroles. And that wasn't a cathedral, more a church that had just got a bit out of hand.

A disappointingly electronic beep announces that the concert is about to start. The Dom is now so full that folding chairs are being hastily arranged at the edges. Your mind quickly discards an obvious observation about the average age of those present and as the first deep bass notes flood the chamber you too look up.

The summer evening light is strong, the brightness and your stillness mean you actually spend a good five minutes trying to make sense of that early cinema, the stained-glass window. Bach's rotational melodies start to form complex waves of sound. You assume it's Bach; even though you can't name any Bach pieces in the actual here and now, it's certainly behaving in what you take to be a Bach-ian manner. Brilliant interlocking harmonic gambits that somehow conspire to render any response redundant. But the organ's near-endless reverberation is also narcotic and you try to read the stained-glass scenes to stave off sleep.

The overarching theme seems to be woe. Tribulation also gets a look-in, stalking characters in the various tableaux. Doubling down on an effortlessly maintained ignorance of biblical details, you carry out the thought experiment that this is your first encounter with the culture of Christianity, that you must – as a stranger in a strange land – make sudden sense of these pivotal narratives.

Women are mothers, or unhappy, or unhappy mothers. Young men are either proud with power, agricultural without speaking parts, or being put upon by rock-carrying peers. One chap in particular seems to be honoured or condemned to stand up on a wooden cross. Whether he's pro or anti isn't entirely clear. Certain people get to glow, others less so. As in the building itself, there's an appeal to light sources from on high, although power itself and the better part of the drama tellingly comes not from above but down on the ground.

But now the invisible hands of the organist are making stabbier chords and more defined melodic directions, you're all woken up and can't resist a smile. History is in the air, and on the move in the cathedral. What a fitting place to become subtly aware of unseen guiding hands with a story to share. Somehow the programme's dance through musical time chimes with some enjoyably vague ideas you have about post-war German character. Above right, you spot the pixellated replacement stained-glass window by Gerhard Richter. Its dotty schematic colours are childlike and computational, its modernity sweet yet somehow stately enough for its setting.

The programme feels like it's now charging through the latter 20th century, and even though you don't recognise the pieces you know the world that birthed them. With the organ now sounding simultaneously like a horn section, cinema strings and glockenspiel, you look back and down and around you.

Finally the waves of sound fade away, applause breaks out and a small man in a brown suit makes an Oz-like appearance up on the balcony, confirming the towering nature of the instrument above. People cheer and he gives two thumbs up, smiling broadly. Human scale is restored, it's a show, a physical play – people, patience and sound.

Awards Night

Well, we're bringing only the most golden threads together tonight, make no mistake about that. A real opportunity to take stock and celebrate. Making something big happen bigger, feel biggest.

In a more concrete sense, this ghastly shindig takes place like clockwork once a year. Your appearance is an emerging unavoidable phenomenon that doesn't yet have a name, but here we are once again – well, yes.

Viewed from the hotel ballroom's balcony, the tables in the main hall look a bit like the wheels of some mechanical leviathan. Fake candles shimmer and indicate the machine's readiness. But no cogs in here tonight, eh? It's all dinner jackets and twitchy necks, shapeless careers solidifying in the over-egged glam.

Wander, wander, not to find but to get through the time. Finally you catch your breath for the first time at the gauchely named 'Star Bar'. Prosecco soldiers are ranked and ready on the counter, don't mind if I do. But even here innocuous choices have minefield-like downsides.

There's Chris. Standard. Already partaking of the bubbly, and as you pad up you catch the tail end of a chat-up line that you'd assumed had been retired by an EU directive around 1995. Amelia? Amerie? Andrea? Anyway, her gently entreating smile at you to replace her in this duologue is admirably professional.

'Chris! Alo-ha…' you offer. This confident-sounding start masks a worry that Chris might be a bit of a doomed choice of companion for tonight's jamboree. Because Chris is not very on-team. He's likely to get out of hand and yell things during the award-giving, which represents the ultimate level of decadence in corporate morality.

You like Chris when he's sober, or at least you distantly approve of his own brand of compromises between time, qualification and money. But something of his devil-may-care attitude freaks you out. You could *be* him inside three years if you don't do something – anything – else. Commitment and compromise end up so tightly wound, and nobody likes a clever hang-around. The ambitious might be ugly in motion, but theirs is the only beauty that's true to its code. Business would rather be profitable than right any day.

'Ready to enjoy the good news about the five-year plan, comrade?' Chris is doing a German accent because it's easier than a Russian one. As most here know only too well, markets are all about reading small signals and Chris's clip-on bow tie is already at a jaunty angle that heralds massive imminent sell-offs.

'Ha! Yes – the big party, one more time. Still – might I bag sir a free drink?'

It's pretty early doors, but Chris's personal crash already seems pencilled in for about 10.15pm, tops – a prediction that even someone as tangentially connected to the company's key product lines as you can predict.

Thus far you've maintained a pragmatic invisibility, been ambiently skilled, gaining a knack of rewriting your job description without anyone noticing – these well-paid duplicities have kept your city life afloat. But, ah, the annual office party – your attendance can never be simply subtext. This is a night for the full-throated pledges of fealty and, with your luck, a horrifying revisitation of the company song.

Platitudes and plates of food. Endless hours of it. It's a shame capitalism is never as bracingly vicious as the economics textbooks claim.

But tonight's a night to celebrate the innovators, so fuck

it, why don't we make this interesting? They've hedged the weather, why not bet on the very roller coasters we build for our hires? Give your family a better tomorrow with the *Cerebus Staffscape 2015 Galacti-Bond*.[1]

Four to seven repeat visits to the champagne-dispersal area later, everything that should be coming together feels like it's coming apart. Money and value and influence flow around the room in liquid, pulsing lights and conversational forms. A *Strictly Come Dancing* pink-blue-ish hue is projected onto every white-shirted surface, rendering the better-looking brokers that bit more Ken doll than they already were. The lighting is intended to function like the bubbly: it's a glue that says 'Tonight, you are all stars' (the 's' should be Bond-villainously sibilant). Communal endeavour is praised to the rafters, despite the fact that most people here have spent all week trying to screw each other over.

Some – the brave, the risk-takers – will be recognised, not from above, but by us all. Well, strictly speaking, it's recognition from the board of directors in their spiritual role as gifted entrail-readers of the share-owners' will. But the broad outline is: a long-destined glory lies within our grasp. We are both Koreas, North and South – lofty zombified nationalism and people who are actually good at stuff. A timeless mission, as we build the imaginary progress of a fictional tomorrow.

Chris slumps at a careworn 45 degrees into the seat next to you with two more of tonight's go-to cocktails, somehow very much in his element.

'Bloody hell… this is longer than the Oscars,' he unloads loudly into a room-sized pause. In a daytime, work-a-day context, Chris's affably focused slave-driving means his team

---

1. Remember to regularly check in to see what condition your terms and conditions are in.

of rapid-rapacity software developers remain pre-eminent. They're the invisible pillars of the success that tonight's event will lionise in the more traditional form of the trading-floor Charlies. But it explains his invite, just the same. Businesses take Chrises in vain at their peril – and their short-termism is rarely that short-sighted.

From his beach-recliner angle, Chris is eyeing Susanna, the Forex queen of Level 11, and you Sherlock that there probably isn't a Mrs Chris. Here every year, yet you always somehow forget that these are also hunting grounds.

Years ago, in a somewhat different place, held together by cheap beer and the nation's fading ideal of an arts education, you'd studied under a series of very different alpha males. Greek philosophy, European Romanticism, Cartesian dualism and heaps of British mathematico-emotionalism. Imperious and exotic notions about life's content and motivations. Categories within categories, details that both explained and divided what little an 18-year-old might know about the world. But delivered with the splendid authority of those truly gifted with social awkwardness.

Ironically, you'd laughed at the parlour-game idea of a division between mind and body back then. Yet look at us now. Double lives are everywhere, simultaneous alterna-yous, onion-like layers with never-touching, parallel goals. Now we're at a poetry reading. Tonight we are corporate boosters with our eye on the prize. If it's 6am, let's just agree to have unlikely and excitable opinions about everything. You and I can be so many.

Back here in the hall of the victors there's only room for the unapologetically present, mind. They even have charming little awards made of plastic to give out – a gender-unfocused statuette for homes that mostly lack for mantelpieces. Breathe, applaud, smile. And the oxygen-plus that fills the room is proper winner-gas, draw deep and think on where you see yourself in five years' time.

A zing of feedback from the lectern snaps your attention back from the largely unfathomable table fascinator that stands proudly, casting malevolent shadows on the pepper mill and mustard dish.

The fizz is beginning to lose its fizzle in your mouth, proof your mood hedge has probably peaked, and yes, the time now starts with a 10. Timing is admittedly all but you could definitely probably quit now, without offending the elders, couldn't you?

'More champagne, sir?'

A pretty if professional smile and big brown eyes. You want to say, 'You're beautiful and not part of this drama and I was like you once, I was outside, and I'm not here either, although I am here, and that's why I'm smiling at you and you're probably a dancer when not catering to the catering and we could run away together and teach yoga in southern Portugal.' But you actually say 'Lovely!' with a borrowed smile, and we're all rebubbled.

Chris has been semi-coherently trying to interest you in the concept of an after-party. He's booked a suite at the hotel, what with having a sensible house too far by train for this kind of night.

You weigh the potential horrors. But in that moment's pause, Stefanie Bickell (12th floor, private lift to the office's mythic sky garden), rising star of complex repackaged degradations, has taken to the stage, wide-eyed and clearly much invigorated with her own award of just 10 minutes previous. She takes the mic with, you've got to say, an adorably naïve gait, given how many important human resource verticals are looking on. For a few moments the whole thing actually feels as gloriously real as television.

'Hi everyone! Isn't this amazing? Whoop! Okay, I am going to read this out properly, I promise... Gary! Don't, you're putting me off. So... exciting! The... 2014 award for Most Innovative Structured Investment Vehicle goes to...'

More in-jokes and outward smiles. The prize-winners' Oscar-ish figurines are featureless, blank and smooth, perhaps another dark clue as to what the future holds. You're not marooned as such, just incapable of delivering on a stated desire to leave. A tall ladder extends out of the back of the stage, which you would jump onto in front of everyone if only it had some rungs. But it has none. Bugger. Would screaming help? Something for the after-party perhaps, but you only live one night bus away so there's really no excuse to stay – and yet not enough impetus to be gone.

With luck and the daily guidance app that nags you not to join the circus or form a cult and knows where you live, you'll make it home again. Somewhere on the way home the two sides of the Venn diagram will blur back into one, and you'll forget everything in the prize of sleep.

Our Voyage Begins at Last

We're badly hit. I mean, really badly. We've lost Carlos, second mate, most of the gravity is failing on decks 12–18… the ship, the ship is really shot… It was the lasers I believe, mostly the lasers, we— I guess I hadn't expected them to have such good lasers.

God, Laura, so many good people. My science officer Velk, just out of the academy. Damn. So much promise, such brilliance. Beautiful too, in his way. He could plot the jump between Tau Ceti and Leonis Minoris in the time it takes me to operate that Italian coffee machine some fool installed on the bridge. This day will live in infamy, I tell you.

God, these alarms never stop, do they? I guess that means we still haven't repressurised the restaurants on Level 18. Those poor guys, no air and no escape.

We outsourced the catering on the advice of the bean counters, and frankly I did it through gritted teeth. But you know what? Turns out the Saureenz might be cheaper than robots but their silver-service skills could go toe-to-toe with anyone I've encountered in a galaxy of dining encounters. So polite, so deft with the sauces and always on top of the specials. I swear, we shall mourn them just as deeply as the regular crew, assuming we ever get this crate back to the station. I shall personally see to it.

I hope you get this vidcom message, Laura – you know I'm totally gonna be there for your graduation. I have such respect for adult education, you know that. I mean, Jesus, I didn't make Captain until I retrained, you know that, right? This is all new, really. I was more on the marketing side of the fleet until four years ago. Funny. But you grow up pretty damn fast in that chair, I can tell you that, particularly on a day like today.

'Support that bulkhead! For God's sake hold firm and get him free! Use the robots!'

Assuming we can re-energise the power grid I'll definitely be there for the ceremony, promise. Sunday, right? It's at the symphony hall?

It's a hell of time for it but you know me, relentlessly upbeat! Maybe after you get your gong, we could, I dunno, take a walk down by the harbour? There's a nice little bistro, Giovanni's I think, we could—

'What do you mean we've lost all power to the shields? Someone get me Hansek in the engine room. I need power!'

The sad part is this ship, this beautiful old girl; she's seen some times. And I'd just personally overseen her complete refitting. New carpets throughout the social areas. Healthier food options in the Vendomats. Pretty state of the art. It's about sharing a commitment, living a promise. I've always placed transparency at the heart of my captaincy. Don't like to blow my own trumpet, Laura, but those internal feedback forms, they don't lie.

What I'm saying is, I think you have to see every setback in the round. Every captain must be big picture. Yes, we've lost the ability to steer the ship, and sure, a lot of people were vapourised in the initial blast, but when they were sucked through the airlocks they left a happy, integrated team.

I want you to know that, assuming we don't crash into the ISS *Globalus*, and assuming we make it back to Earth, I'm really a pretty stand-up guy. I know we've only known each other a few weeks but I'm very supportive of other people's goals. *Your* goals, Laura.

Well, this is me. Fridays are always a horror, right? Ha. I

should really see if that hatch is still—. Ah. Well, really hope we can touch base on the weekend. Love you. There. I've said it.

"OUR VOYAGE BEGINS AT LAST."   *p.* 28.

Trimmed Back: A Few Notes From the Brainstorm

'Discomfort sensitising shave mousse'
Nice... but bit of a double-edged sword? Twin virtues? Manliness? Maybe replace 's' with 'z' spelling, for added power?

'Smooth glide... smooth ride'
Is the cowboy mentality still a thing in 2018? Visuals look a bit too 'Brosnan'...

'Age-attenuating action'
... love the science-y angle (strong) & sounds purposive without overt narcissism (win). Negs: too brainy?

'Fissionbalm smoothing layer'
Love it! Possible atom-and-particles-type graphics? 'The world rotates around you with new...' A tad cold maybe?

'Stubble-terminating powergel'
Pros: confident, declarative. Cons: bit heavy? Maybe balance with an offsetting virtue? 'Gently terminating'?

'Nick-proof depilating masque'
Possible application confusion? Man in the Mask? (too Jacko?) Positive: 'Nick' is popular guy's name. Nicely projects social/career competency.

'Mandation – now with smoothing guy granules'

Mandated = governance metaphor – poss. copy: 'decision makers use…' more than just make-up? Makers – traditional male skills – alignment with carpenters and tradesmen (strong). Power from within? Reduces sense of the superficial. 'Stay in control of the granular details with…' suggests complete control. Love it!

15 Words, Max.

'Tell us a fact about yourself.' In a different context this question could have come across as a little bit threatening. Give us a name and we'll say no more about it. Where were you on the morning of the 13th? And so on.

But as the final field to be completed on a luxury car raffle entry, the question was given to causing a more positive quickening of the blood. A happy anticipation that here at last was a chance to buck the fickle ways of Lady Fate. An open goal, really. Just win over the judges' hearts and minds with something authentic, honest, even funny.

Jane emptied this morning's entries over the grey laminate desk. The luxury car entries were a weekly highlight in a fairly repetitive summer admin job, working at a clearing house full of retail competitions. A fragment of more or less every aspect of contemporary life was being offered in prize form from somewhere within this unremarkable building outside Croydon. From microwaves that roast to holiday villas in seaside resorts long past their best, sacks full of completed prize-draw forms arrived daily.

Jane had long settled on the theory that it was all driven by context. You had to picture the scene. Somewhere in an airport terminal was a slowly revolving and undoubtedly red Ferrari, capturing perfectly the pre-holiday sense that things were definitely going your way. For just a tenner flutter, you drive off into a new world.

By Jane's reckoning the decision to even enter the prize draw had to be accompanied by a certain level of personal expectation management: 'It's just a bit of fun.' You were, after all, playing about in the same probabilistic neighbourhood as being plurally struck by lightning – the bit where numbers, good or bad, get a bit pointed. A little self-deprecating laugh, then, as biro bites down on card.

As with any seemingly throwaway task, it soon dawns that a couple of minutes of actual concentration are required. Name, address, email – sure. A ticked agreement to appear in any eventual publicised award ceremony. But then there it is, at the end: 'Tell us a fact about yourself (15 words, max.).'

Jane had dined out on so many of the scrawled responses that filled this box. Insofar as you'd actually want to dine out in Croydon.

There was something about a supercar's inherent overemphases, its portal-like promise of another world, that brought out the entire spectrum of human experience and ambition in these 15-word pitches. Sudden displays of raw emotion; tentatively drawn connections to the world of high-net-worth driving; hints of insider smarts; comically ill-judged unburdenings. And always a gem or two.

'I have risen at 5am daily since the age of 17.'

'I love my kids, Bethany, Davis and Tarabelle.'

'I once met Mika Häkkinen at Silverstone.'

'I was at school with the drummer of Culture Club.'

Jane had often wondered, with a slight smile, if the average punter would be disappointed to learn that the entries were being judged – well, read and reviewed – by an arts student who couldn't even drive. True, the prize draw carried the endorsement of a certain car-obsessed TV presenter, which was a little disingenuous. But nowhere was it actually stated that the winner would be chosen by motoring's self-appointed high priest, even if he appeared in a loose-fitting American flying jacket and beaming smile on all the promotional literature.

Perhaps it was just a condition of entry that one surely

believed such a momentous prize could only be awarded after sombre judgement by elders and betters.

'I have a signed copy of every book by David Icke.'

'My wife and I will have been married for 35 years in April.'

'I have a collection of 300 Airfix planes in my loft.'

'I love all humanity equally, taking no part.'

At this last, Jane's eyes skidded to a halt. The first five words had teased a smile – the jarring presence of fading hippiedom, or worse, recent Alpha-course graduate?

But it was the final clause that brought Jane up short. 'Taking no part'. What did it mean? That austere yet broad-reaching tone didn't belong here in the world of macho material hopefulness. Weird. Weirder, the rest of the details were completely commonplace. Christopher Davis, 12 Langley Mansions, Oldwood Road, Lancaster.

'Taking no part' – was it a joke? A stab at religiosity? No, it was far too odd to be parody or satire. Jane read it again, softly but aloud. It actually felt difficult to say, like a piece of alien syntax from another time, another world. She didn't want to read the others now. The task's usual jolly mood was broken, yet a spell was cast, not from above, but speaking direct from history.

A coffee was needed. Jane put the entry down and started to think what would happen if it won the prize.

The office kitchen's radio interjected with Earthly dramas. A plucky migrant rescue story, involving feats of faith and travel. A recently-repaired political career whose unlikely second act involved rock-climbing, now compromised by an ill-judged affair. An intelligent car with a death wish. Something upsetting about tennis.

And now *this*. How could this second coming, if that was what it was, compete with all that? How could you be epic without sounding utterly mad? Revelations were a series of detonating roadside dramas, not peace-shaped missives from above.

Jane put 'Christopher Davis' to one side. Perhaps there were other strangenesses lurking among the day's remaining entries. But they were the usual mishmash of terrestrial hopes and dreams.

An email dinged. 'Entries sorted?' David, her supervisor, had more stuff for her to do. She briefly toyed with the idea of raising her queries over the entry, and then realised that there was no way of broaching them without seeming hopelessly invested in… what exactly?

Where was this day going? Something had been unplugged. Language had lost its invisibility and was proving troublesome. She felt a slight feeling of being overwhelmed. 'Taking no part'; such a powerful statement. Presence in the shape of retreat. Overbearing in its myth-making, the phrase tripped up the everyday patter of declaration and conversation. Too bright a light from a door you regret propping open.

Could meek and mild really bridge two different worlds? Could personal transcendence be reached at near 185mph among those kings of the petrolhead kingdom? It was a dazing possibility. Yes, it could win – no, it had to win – this was a necessary intervention, a righteous disruption in the usual order of things.

Jane shivered and tingled despite the stuffy warmth of the room. A power surged across her head and behind her shoulders as she looked guiltily around at her co-workers. Her involvement would be unseen, unknown. The entry form in her hand was somehow both ticket and revelation, beginning and ending, promise and destiny joined.

She would move in a mysterious way, then, guided by a new sense of purpose, one whose magic was making her beam like never before. She would make this happen, guided not from above, but still splendid and directed, true as an arrow, yet taking no part.

'*I am in the habit of spending part of every Sunday afternoon alone, in musing on the magnificence of nature and the moral dignity of man.*'

Complexities at the ParagraphBar

(哲学的 居酒屋)

Yoko is laughing at the inflated mortar board on Charles's head. It does look funny, squashed down on his sizey bonce like a swimming aid. Hardly striking a note of academe, but then the music is pretty damn loud in here.

'You're going to the bar? An Asahi if they haven't got anything else, alright? Arigato Frank-san!'

The mic is passed on, in what's become increasingly a blur in the last 60 minutes, oh blast, 'No more Camus!' you josh. Try to stay on it. Sushi sets as ever proving no defence against the birthday boozy set.

Back from the bar, and returning through the airlock-style doors, ah here we go, and yes, it's always the big hits. Florence is up next, her eyes scan the listings for a fave to recite, while we all wait for the good stuff.

The screen, whose lack of focus is either a clever dig at the performances or, as you suspect, just an ageing CRT buried in the wall, changes from blue to pink as the letters start appearing. Florence is hot, and she knows that we know she never looks hotter than when reciting Camus. She waves the mic unprofessionally below her chin, hardly the stance of a world-renowned miserablist with the world at his feet, but it's a winsome display.

It's also worse yet better that her poise is slightly undermined by her inability to read it with the rhythm of the original French. Nevertheless, highly tangible levels of charm fill the room, as Florence's brown eyes follow the dancing ball above the words, until you're just a little bit devastated.

'Provide to us for a look of eternal I think beauty, unbearable minute we would like extend over the entire time, to drive us to despair...'

This being a *paragraphbar* at the rougher end of Lil' Tokyo, they've used some godawful on-the-fly translation for the content, so this is French philosophy that's come to London from Tokyo via Chinese economy class. The maddening mangle of the text is part of the fun of course. And it wouldn't work for anything but continental philosophy, where a certain showy verbalising is very much *de rigueur*. The translation's failure is sort of what sets it free. Or something.

Florence is on to the hits now and Charles the postgrad looks a bit transfixed. Anna, who seems to be his new 'possibly', is dividing her gaze between them both, cautionary steel and righteous girl-love. Frank's on the end of the sofa, far too far gone to follow the nuance of the performance by this point, but throws over the inflatable umbrella, which Florence begins to twirl endearingly as she delivers the next line:

'Nothing but this slow trek through the detour of art, to rediscover, man's work is first opened the image simple and wonderful thing two or three in the heart of his existence.'

We whoop enthusiastically, secretly a bit terrified of who's going to have to follow this. Flo is in full flow. Yoko and Anna click their fingers and sway a little; their faces flicker with a campfire brightness, smiling as mid-20th-century ethical insights melt like marshmallows.

'They will not be really willing to die except for free men. Therefore, they do not believe it completely dead.'

You take a long draught of bubbly, savoury beer, letting the mood wash over you.

'Thrift and loneliness: working conditions for I have become a thing of the monastic life at all times. With the exception of thrift, they so

*much so, what I am the violence themselves, the work is contrary to
my nature…'*

Maybe it's the booze that's the dark matter holding all of this
together, grammatically speaking? I mean, it's definitely a fun
and novel way to encounter the classics of post-1930 thinking,
and yes, you must come in here almost twice a month despite
half-heartedly always decrying the idea. Perhaps it's actually a
bit more sensual than your protestations to the contrary would
admit?

You gaze over at Rufus. He's 29, that pivotal age where you
can still imagine your mind a lava'd foundry of the new and
daring, despite having spent the most recent decade mooching
about on the fading carpets of academe. You have some fun and
balletic arguments with Rufus at the university, but he's a little
more cloudy in social situations. A brooding red wine in one
hand, but jacket still on, he seems to be making a physical nod
to his own chief philosophical contribution to date. Of course,
the ellipma '…,' never really took off as a mainstream theoretical
concept. But as a social marker for one who is perpetually
readied not to leave… well, maybe it has legs after all? *'Jeremy
frowned, umbrella in hand as he stood at the bar, caught in an
ellipma.'* Perhaps things will work out for Rufus.

Yoko has taken over at the mic. Being Japanese, she's
beautifully gluing the evening's disparate mechanics back
together by conducting as she reads the various
Nipponosophies being generated on the TV screen in a knock-
off of Comic Sans. You've never enjoyed Camus as much as
right now, and you notice the cutesy drum machine being
piped through recessed speakers for the first time, as it
unconsciously guides Yoko's delightful oration:

*'Society, cannot when he was away on artists who forged their own
others and also be from the beauty of the middle and tear yourself,*

do without him. A true artist is the reason why I have not seen you down. Understanding rather than the judge has mandated them...'

A young European woman dressed as a geisha enters the room gently, so as not to interrupt Yoko, refills the bowl of sweets on the low table, picks up the empties, bows and leaves. If we've chewed through an entire bowl we've been here a while alright.

But what of your own work? What contribution have you made to the map of understanding? The Philosophy of Leaving? Hard to see you ever really pitching this to the departmental bigwigs. 'It's naught but heftless posturing and journalese, Christopher,' you can imagine them saying, before making disparaging references to Alain de Botton.

But it's that same original thought that's born at 11.47pm every time you're here at philosophy's own nightly song contest. How cities have got so good at providing compact and effective little illusions, pools of possibility that somehow strengthen, elevate and undermine you all at once. When fun attacks. How every attempt to escape the everyday necessitates some sort of further moral compromise. When freedom attacks. Ways to waste your time that evolve and elaborate, heightening the sense of what you've failed to get done, just as they unlock another 'achievement'. Fill your life with this, then write it down. For God's sake, at least write it down. And then perhaps, one day, somewhere under unlikely haircuts, the young and drunk will sing along.

Energy Levels

Boom bang a bang, doof thud schwaaah… quite the noisy morning, is this. Smiling going on everywhere, and only 7.49am showing on the counter. The doors open to a factory-sized room, beats flood out and light floods in, bouncing off a mass motion of colourful Lycra.

Jim turned back to me, his face triumphant; this was clearly his tribe. 'Feel that energy!'

'I thought we'd agreed not to use the word "energy"…?' I said, mock sour.

'Sorry. Ha! Yes! You and that! Howzabout "buzzy"? "Pulse-y"?' Jim smiled and started throwing frenzied shapes.

The atmosphere was overwhelming in a way that was hard to fathom. The familiar rendered unfamiliar. A breakfast nightclub, a sober madness. Bits of songs I knew, remixed for added brightness and clarity. My hair was still damp from the shower.

'So Ellie… is the one over there in the tutu and top hat?' I asked.

'Esta – her name's Esthermoon but she shortens it to Esta – amazing ener- spirit…'

'I really don't want to seem all difficult about it…'

Jim and I marked a pause in the early morning frugging to pick our espressos up from the tiny coffee stand at the back of the hall. Shower. Coffee. Rave. A slight smile I can't suppress is finding the very idea of being here amusing, much as I want to fight it.

'I know – you uptight *Guardian* types!' Jim is already high on the social buzz, the espresso is just a finishing move. His gaze smilingly passes on to two passing glittery 20-somethings who are glugging back fruited water before returning to the fray.

'I *am* here,' I point out, 'raving with you. We two, together, raving. At 7.56am.'

I am shouting a little to be heard over the PA, but a glittering smile from just over there achieves the inner silence you sometimes know you need. The goal is to let go. Knock back the coffee and jump off the side of the self.

Fragments of Stevie Wonder borne aloft under euphoric new wings are pounding out of the speakers. However new it is, dance music always seems to trade on a shared nostalgia. Seemingly, some parallel version of the Nineties is happening again all around you. It's not so much that time means you lose faith in fun, it's just that the confusion of having history remixed means you're not sure which you is supposed to be enjoying themselves. I begin to think I should probably definitely stop thinking so much and keep dancing.

"HOW I ONCE WENT DOWN THE MIDDLE."

That shell that you keep painting new things on, the mask that tapes so comfortably into place, that finds value in everything but money – these little defences are gone the moment you start moving. If you can just tamp down your brain from throwing together inner monologues about the inherent dishonesty of appeals to shamanic tradition. Because if you let yourself taste the edges of this, they're good. Sugary, bouncy castle; whizzy, good.

Another unfolding London surprise, another little break found in the fence. If sticking around has been about anything, it's been the attempt to somehow renew yourself in the mirrors held up by 8.5 million neighbours. Cheaper than psychotherapy and a good deal less complicated; just try to catch a glimpse of who you are in what you do.

And yet here you are, choking on your own wisdom and the gritty coffee. The sheer joy of these people. Waves of exultation sweep across the room as the stab chords of an early Noughties dance hit you vaguely recognise start to work their magic. 'Tonight's the Night'? 'At Nite'? 'Feel My Nite'? Ironically it's only 8.11am, but look at Jim – he's having the time of his life, a blur of diagonals in front of a girl who might have been Miss Romania. Sure beats project managing a canal-side factory in Hull.

A girl in bright red ballet clothes is excelling at hoop gymnastics to generalised whooping from the 800-plus dancers. You find yourself mesmerised – even by the standards of a city hellbent on showing off, this is leading-edge stuff.

All these years, the morning has largely remained the preserve of carbohydrates, caffeine and the raw stimulation of information. News and fumbling, every day a chaotic curtain-raiser at best.

But *sans* booze and plus music, you find your body and mind are going on something of a 'getting to re-know you' session. How old would 20-year-old you have expected to be before reading about 'mindful disco'? So, stillness in the grey matter, and lissom limbs hoping to gain compliments for vivacity. It shouldn't be possible and they won't believe you in the office, but then you work from home.

Not From Above

It begins with a blanket. You momentarily want to hear your inner voice confidently declare that the best things always do. But you can't think of any other things that begin with a blanket, and also you've only owned a blanket for the last three hours, so it all seems a bit premature.

Breathe in, slowly and inwardly, don't get ahead of yourself now. And yet despite the near absolute lack of physical motion, events are clearly occurring, great things are afoot. Looking out and down the hill a scattering of semi-committed clouds passingly obscures the summer sun and the temperature begins to dip. London summer typical, all change and no drama.

You can see about as far as Kennington from up here, should you so wish. The mind's very occasional ability to get all the senses working together as a team – it's better than an afternoon risking death in a theme park. From the air cooling your fingertips as they hold the plastic cup of wine, to the warmth you can sense from the companion who thrillingly seems quite relaxed on the blanket next to you. Your eyes soak up distance and hope it's generating actual perspective at long last.

Your ears, meanwhile, are doing a grand job. Insects, your companion's breathing, distant cars near The Spaniards Inn, a budget flight soaring upwards with its heart set on Magaluf. And then, silently, a hand reaches out for yours, absently full of purpose.

For a few brief seconds all these things connect, and time slows down as if tipping you a wink: 'Oh, we see what you've managed there, nice work.' Slow time, no fad for once, for stillness can be a mood. A series of unfolding possibilities, without announcements. Don't think, just let it happen. Not from above, but from within.

Aksturmeðvitundarlauslogn

(Driving Unconscious Calm)

True peace of mind has an inner rhythm, Stefan. You'll start to sense that beat in the space around you, a pulse beneath your feet on the pedals, connected to the tarmac under your wheels.

Not still, no, but imagine attaining the pureheadedness that comes with true, carefree rapidity. And letting go – of fear, yes. Certainly fear. The steering column also. This is a recently serviced BMW 3 Series. Cruise control as standard. Very comfortable, and really the perfect vehicle for your first *róa*.

On the R436 you can be a graceful nomad, a wise man. Serenity comes in many forms, and average traffic density is only six vehicles per month. Please advance the in-car player to 17 minutes in – a little light techno, locally sourced, will back my words. A duo from Hafnarfjörður, only in their early twenties when they wrote this, inspired by the open vistas of the lava plains. Reach out, touch the fascia whilst letting your face reach up to the open sun roof. Let the gods gather in the windscreen, in maximum achievable safety. Bracing means alive. There's a left in 4 kilometres which I wouldn't miss, *eff why i*.

How's the temperature? Murmur your needs lightly, eyes gently closed; feel your self-consciousness melt away, it's all voice-controlled. Your blood will pulse in harmony with the soothing in-car environment. Forty-five mph is probably fine for this stretch of the *Þingvallavegur* – it's pretty straight. Route 436-different-words-for-calm, if you like.

And the elk bring a sense of the contemplative, do they not? Of our connection to nature, an animal belonging as you carve your own way through the bracing emptiness. Imagine their eyes, mutely accepting of your task, a timeless wisdom that's alive in all nature. Individually (as you'll discover at speeds regularly in excess of 85mph), it's not perhaps entirely about wisdom. But let's imagine they want the best for you as those shoulders really start to ease and relax.

Is the blindfold chafing? You should have said, the strap is adjustable. We use island-spun cotton to get a nice soft feel for the deepest meditation or *hugleiðsla*. Now, is that better? Great. Let your mind wander again, we're doing just fine.

If you reach gently to the right you'll find the electric window controls. Just a few millimetres and feel that air purity flood in. Careful, though: at this speed the sound can be a little overwhelming.

Can I be briefly encouraging? You've already clocked up 43 kilometres. Stillness can be really moving, no? Ben Stiller, when he was here filming last year, managed 39, tops. But I'm distracting you. Let your mind feel the road, like an invisible track running between your feet as we gently navigate towards whatever must surely lie ahead. The hills and the valleys are always distant, yet always nearing. The road is as straight as your commitment; being is becoming, becoming is driving. How's the heated seat? Not too off-putting? Good.

Try to stay defocused, but engaged, like a child fathoming the workings of a magnetic toy. There will be a brief pause for refreshments at one of the nationally mandated picnic areas on the 436. I'm so proud of how you're doing – and this, your first time.

Let's try for fifth gear, shall we? It can be so uplifting. It's a confident step, a little milestone, if you'll forgive the pun. Let the relaxation dominate and overwhelm your senses. It's best if the wheel feels a little loose under your fingers too, like a lover's careless caress...

So, so very good. There's nothing to see and yet it's all around you, do you feel the uplift? Out of body, but in the car, out of body, yet here we are. Very good. I can feel your shoulders loosening, you're driving–unconscious–calm. Self is overcome, and panic is only for the still, as they observe your progress from the relative safety of the roadside. She really bites down on the road as you nudge over 75, I find.

My instructions will get softer from this point, until our thoughts alone, connected, guide our onward fate. I once remained silent for 12 weeks at a Vipassanā yoga retreat outside Helsinki, yet my thoughts gained such amplitude and clarity. There's a gentle left coming up, but you'll feel my whispered breath when the time comes.

If you feel down to the right you'll sense the Velcro wrist straps – when you're ready, just let your hands drop from the wheel and snap into the clips. You're so connected to the road now, your spine is the centre of our motion, your feet will make our fate, I feel sure of it.

The mind is a marvel, Stefan, and if only you could see your face as it appears to me in the rear-view mirror. It's a picture of evolving if unconscious calm, a gathering nothing, a sure line that's an inner smile. Don't speak – I'm right, aren't I?

Glory, Deferred, But Undimmed

*Keep this book with you at all the times of life. The
thinkings of Shining Eternal General-President Gerjalda
Kazarimov will be as guides, moments of momentous
inspiration. Perhaps two of your goats are poorly. Maybe
your sister lacks for motivation at the aluminium works,
or your mother has once again failed to win the
Puzhkavian Golden Spheres Lotto. Life in our great
nation is always a struggle, but a struggle embraced leads
to the happy swaddling of knowledge. And this book, the
Sutranamara, is brimful of learnings, ones that support
and guide, lean in and whisper with confident insistence.*

My people! Take down the bit from your horse's mouth! For
otherwise how will your horse speak and impart wisdom? Hold
your ride close, always. Our ancestors birthed us as the proud
horse-riding nomads of the Puzhkavian plains and that destiny
must be embraced once more. But the ride will be wilder,
and like them we must throw off the yokes of bridle, bit and
saddle. The nation demands it, as we work harder than ever,
particularly at the Samsung-PuzhkaviaTel joint-venture mines
and at the site of the Kazarimov Palace of the People's Victory
in Abrûlz.

It is said that when a poem is beautiful it is true. But do
not the philosophers also say that when a poem is penned by
your humble leader, it will contain calls to greatness? In every

poem therefore lies the light of direction. I have also written a complete list of the things that you should do in boldface on the inside cover of this edition, just to be clear. Freedom and action – petals that coexist within the flower of duty.

April is my name! For in glorious spring, the blossoms are fulsome, like red-cheeked warriors at last returned from distant yet glorious battle-making. April will herald a redoubling of nerve. Every child of reading age will sing a happy song, from the texts that are newly printed and rushed to every school. Hope is in the air. The weapons inspectors have likely left. April is now to be called Gerjalda.

Though our new Mausoleum of the Eternal Presidency is topped with a 400-metre gold chturetta, you shouldn't focus on its dazzling colour (which can be espied as far away as the iridium mines of Dursk or the aluminium smeltworks of Nankangaz). No, the material's colour matters not compared to where it points. Wisdom accrued, not from above, but in the body of myself, your Eternal President. And with my cousin Dzokhva, People's Secretary for the Propagation of Civic Dreams, together we have wrought this tribute to what might be achieved in life and in death. Stare not at the base but the point, to gain daily focus and guidance.

Intention and expression, let them be like the twin pillars supporting the expensive gold roof atop the house of your leaders. As intention brings order, so expression frees love. And what love is greater than that for the mother of our Eternal President, Her Holiness Magazda Volnykovka? How her beautiful eyes gaze down watchfully on the children of our nation, from above every mantelpiece, and in the official hand-embroidered picture that is available in our capital city's many gift shops.

That smile, whose magical combination of a nurse's care and a soldier's steel inspires every child that tarries below it. How it mirrors the very shape of our border with Ruvniyistan, in its drama, determination and contention. The humble violence of steadfastness; let it be yours – like the incursions of tempestuous lovers, when we discover our faces afresh. And we read in her face a simple and earnest determination that you shall surely do as you must.

Your humble leader has fought in all the wars, including the ones you've pictured only in dreams. The ones between your wife and her neighbour with the coveted headscarf, its embroidered scenes of horse dancing that set tongues a-wagging. The battle will rage and I will lead, always taking my people to victory. We will switch direction when our opponents think they have won, being of full voice in the barren valleys as well as in the biting winds of the bare and epic plains. It's all I can – and everything I will – do.

Do not fear the mountain as you labour upon its treacherous pathways, or clear its gnarled forests. Mount Kíszkan was named for its benevolent eye o'er the nation. Yes, the fatal pathways of its north-facing ascent form stories the children love and the closely guarded military-industrial facilities near its peak shall not be spoken of here. But my fellow Pushkavianari! Soon we shall together complete the Olympic-standard ski resort and associated retail facilities that will set this great nation on a collision course with the respect and success we deserve. Your many sacrifices are already medals upon my heart.

I am Wolf! Protecting my pack is my very nature, core to my being. My being President perpetual, I must bite into enemies, scent coming difficulties on the breeze and attend many foreign summits. Like my wolf brothers I stand firm, and bay at the moon and the stars in leadership, until they hear and respect our voices, our demands. With you, my pack, at my side, our future is whatever I imagine, our beliefs in me are strong, your direction is clear and true. Onward!

Moving On

24 June 2016

Dear all,

Just a few words from me, on what is, after all's said and done, both a sad day and a new start, a chance to listen again as we reach out and look forward.

For, onward we're propelled. Even today, this difficult today we're having. But still. Ever the New Radicals. Never more than when it's been against our will – surely, that's the finest thing we've ever had?

I know that together we have done things. The achievements have been many. Samantha and I often speak of them, between bouts of tennis and laughter, we remember and look out across the lawn. 'Things!' we say, and hold hands, thinking of Andy Murray. Presently, someone arrives with a letter or drinks.

This has been a difficult time. There is no question about that. Or around that. Recent events have overshadowed the light that hasn't yet come to fall on the shape of all the achievements there have been. Profoundly sorry. But that's okay. This is modern Britain. We have the present, between us and among us. The country remains a guest list that our names are carved upon. I've asked George and yes, it's fine. They serve ice-cold margaritas on Necker Island. And if I've learned one thing, it's to say 'why shouldn't we', of all people?

Sandrine and I often speak of them. The brightest and best. The many ways in which we've unlocked that potential. Modern things for all, the way pop stars can walk the streets, unafraid, Irish too, warmly. This isle, this endless moment. The things we'll achieve, in the time I've already had, heated and yellow, in a bag, strapped tightly to my ankle. Safety first, for we're a people ready for anything, robust and steady.

And that's what gives me confidence. It gives *Sally* and me strength. With Europe behind us and yet somehow all around us, like a fog that guides, not from above, I've got to say: we're well-placed and humming a melody for the ages. Beverley Knight. Jools Holland. Jim Davidson. Debbie McGee. The time has never been more now. I'd like to thank everyone. It's been an honour to serve.

Wonderful.

Yours,

D.C.

Good Hunting, Will

The southern end of Piccadilly at 4pm on a weekday – I was wandering and wondering. There's a certain breezy freedom to the city between three and four, the streets clear of lunching office workers, leaving the sparseness of mid-Nineties video games.

Perhaps it's the feeling that no one on the street at this hour can possibly be doing anything important. Or conversely, that the people you do see are so wealthy that their power defies easy comprehension. A Barbour jacket hides so many professions. Still, somehow the city seems to sense this shared rudderlessness, and together we commitment-phobes march on, gently failing to adequately fill the pavements.

Passing the galleries and seasonal tourists clumped together composing photographs. But moving on, the streets eventually reassert themselves like temporary tributaries breaking free from the morning's long gridlock. I finally got into gear as up ahead I spied the destination.

It was half-four. No harm in getting there a bit early. Scan the joint, a cheap avant-pint to take the edge off of things, perhaps. The meeting was to take place in a chain pub off Gloucester Road, just around the corner from that home of other extinct species, the Natural History Museum. But must think positive.

In cities this size it's all about finding your niche among the many on offer and the determination to jump in. Activities for every taste, you don't have to be like everyone else, but there are directories to help you find your tribe. DIY-robot badger-baiting on Hampstead Heath? Why not. Poetry as anger-management technique. Gambling workshops for the under-fives. Just sign up, go along and see what happens.

Walking in, the Stevenson's Rocket possessed that epic emptiness of the chain pub in the afternoon, marrying architectural excess with more limited ambitions on the food and beverage front. I stood at the long ferry-like bar and ordered a pint of something mild.

The place had seemingly hundreds of empty tables but the best spot, on a raised dais at one end, was annoyingly already taken. Early... but not that early, it seems.

The figure who'd bagged it just had to be Will, aka will.01@lovepioneers.org.uk, the guy I'd encountered on the Meetup website two weeks previously. The zero-one seemed to signal ambition, at least. Or maybe we'd all be given numbers at the meeting? It's supposedly a group effort, in any case, that's part of the process – such as the website described it, anyway. A few more pint holders began to gather and for once a group of men all seemed to be early attendees to an emotional commitment.

'Hello! Great! Right, name badges on! Fab. Simon, lay out the map of West Six, would you, thanks.'

Alan, Dave, Chris, Thomas, Dave, Rich and so on, 11 middle sort of every-men, penning our names on stickers, wary but getting into it.

Will was hard to place at first, aged between, what, 38 and 50, maybe? His short brown hair had the ashy highlights popular with TV naturalists. The North Face body warmer, a solid choice too, fatigues for the civvy street adventurer.

Will's assistant Simon tacked a large map of Greater London to the pub table. Will leant over to smooth it out and as he removed some small red plastic flags from his bumbag, I caught a quick glimpse of the iconic logo of a Swiss Army penknife and some indelible markers nestled within.

'Right, I think we'll get started. I'm Will – head of Love Pioneers, and you, everybody here... are all vets –' he paused for dramatic effect and leant forward with both hands on the table, 'for we're all veterans of the dating wars, are we not, gentlemen?' The accompanying smile was upbeat, and as welcoming as it was simultaneously undermined by the content of the observation.

'Match.com? Come on, hands up.'

Two Daves and a Rich raised their hands with rueful smiles.

'*Guardian* "soul" mates?' he asked, making it three words. Everybody but Thomas raised their hands. 'Oh-Kay Cu-pid?' Chris, Alan and myself raised our hands.

'Oh-Kay Stu-pid more like!' crowed Will in what was clearly a well-worn bon mot. He continued, conspiratorially: 'We all know there's got to be a better way, right?'

A few nods, a history with common features. Yet somehow the 'stupid' had leaked out of the sentence, rebounding off the upturned faces. Bonhomie momentarily stretched thin. And this tiny overreach would be echoed in more dangerous forms over the coming days and nights. Such long days, and complex, difficult nights.

'What chance do we stand, alone? Am I right? It's hell out there. You know the stats. You'd be better off going on Dragon's Den than most dates in this town. But if we work together? Together... we've got a chance. A bloody good chance. Oh yes, my friends, together is how we're going to win the dating.'

Will paused to point at one of the small flags, which was in place at the bottom of Chandos Place, just before you hit the Strand.

'Now lads, this may look like the perfect location, right? Central, easy for her to get to from the office... Nicely done. Pub that does food? Good, strong choice, yes?'

With a sudden swish, Will knocked all the little flags off their hopeful positions on the streets of central London.

'No! Wrong! It's not gonna work! You haven't a hope! Simon – tell 'em...' Will wheezed a little and sat back, while Simon stood up to address us in his place.

'Lemon Tree pub, on Tuesdays it has a live music night...' his voice was flat-toned but confiding, 'a local running team go in there for a wind-down around 7pm... they're all quite athletic. It gets real rowdy. It's... it was hell—'

He trailed off. No more need be said. We sipped, pondered and stared at the paper city. This was our first step into a new mindset, a new approach. We were about to learn the true power of shared intel, coordinated male endeavour and the previously unsung role of map-reading in modern romance.

•

A month later and I can honestly say we really are no longer merely daters. We have truly become love pioneers. We even have a song, written by Anthony (Love Pioneer 04), a graduate of the very first intake. Our ethos is completely analogue. 'Happier app-less!' is the motto, undistracted by technology yet proud of our emotional technique.

True, a good mantra also papers over a few fears. You just keep repeating it under your breath until your heart rate's behaving.

I've never been particularly physically minded but here we are – Chris, Dave and myself – gripping a series of connected ropes and pulleys that we've just tapped into the side of the railway bridge at Charing Cross. We're about 45 feet above the street, because – and this is where you have to just go with me a little – the fourth pioneer on our team, Alan, is about to appear outside the window where Ellie, the current object of his affections, is having a glass of wine with her friend Sarah. It's early doors still, but it seems to be going to plan.

My hands are clad in cheap builders' gloves as I hang on to the side of the building, one part of the little counterweight system that's propelled Alan and a fairly cheap ukulele up outside the windows of Stems Wine Bar. One of the many things I've learned as a love pioneer is that there's no love without fear. You've got to open yourself up to vulnerability, both emotionally and physically. It's also a great moment to recall the stirring lyrics of our Pioneers song:

> *All for love and love for all,*
> *For every gal loves a pioneer,*
> *The things we do, will stand us tall,*
> *It could be love, it feels like fear…*

I remembered leader Will first playing back the group's song on some travel speakers at our second get-to-know-you session and realising we'd become a unit for the very first time. Quite a nice tune, as it goes. Upbeat.

Spending more time around a group of adult men, acquaintances not yet friends, you quickly realise the key role played by small signals and subtle cues. Did our increasing confidence draw directly from Will's perennially outdoorsy wardrobe? And was his belly laugh a sign that things were going well, or badly? We learned mutual responsibility, looking out for each other; I guess without a football team or sporting past, I'd simply kind of missed all this.

Will was persuasive. You found yourself repeating fragments of his monologues at the oddest times. 'If you don't want to learn new things about you, how can you learn new things about someone else?' went the Pioneers' adage. 'When your pulse is up… you're ready for love,' was another. Camaraderie glued it all together somehow.

For how else would we have successfully completed the part-underwater *Operation Veronica* for Chris back in October? Or the four-nights-atop-a-barn-in costumes that became *For the Love of Debbie*? (Surely Dave's finest hour to date?)

I looked up and across at Dave, who had a foothold on an office window about 8 feet away and was leaning back in his harness, checking in no doubt on the Arsenal iPhone app. He didn't seem at all fazed by our current mission or indeed his physical location. And truth be told, that'd been one of the revelations of the group. Surprisingly, being entirely among men in the cause of being among (a) woman opened your eyes to the strengths and oddities of your own side.

I gave the rope between us a little tug.

'How's he doing up there, Dave?' I whispered as loudly as could still be effective over traffic.

'Magic!' Dave winked. 'He's just turned up. Almost show time!'

Chris's voice, a little lost to traffic noise, wafted up from some 12 feet below me.

'Has he delivered the payload?'

'Just about to!' I smiled, entirely unsure of anything but my unwavering belief in the little bolts that Steve, now based at ground level, had come and drilled in earlier, during his lunch hour. Before his current position at the Youth Hostel Association, Steve had worked in a hardware shop and could speak powerfully about tools, physical tolerances and adhesion levels.

I looked up again and saw Alan making the agreed 'W finger' sign with his left hand, so Dave and I leant back on our ropes a little to pull him into the 'readiness position'. As the opening bars of Robbie Williams' seminal 'Angels' could be heard coming from Alan's ukulele you could dimly sense the growing impact of this act of ur-pioneering.

A group of onlookers, presumably including our target Ellie, had gathered at the windows as members of the bar staff prised the windows open – either to enact a rescue or facilitate better smartphone angles, it wasn't entirely clear. Alan's voice was a surprise too – a rich baritone that proved a neat counterpoint to the tinny sound of the bright yellow ukulele. Ellie was surely his. At the very least he'd get an Advanced Love Pioneer (Dedication At Heights) badge from Will. I found myself smiling. Get us!

Some two minutes later we started feeding the rope rapidly through our hands in concert, as Alan was hauled bodily into the wine bar above by black-shirted staff members. Storming the Bastille at last. I looked down to see Will smiling broadly from the pavement. He made an 'O' with his fingers and took a swig from the miniature bottle of Midori liqueur he keeps in his utility belt for victorious moments.

An hour or so later and our merry band were ensconced in a pre-booked area at the back of the Blackened Barrels behind Waterloo Station, celebrating Alan's big night.

In the fog of battle, of course, there always remain questions over the wider prosecution of the campaign. When is a win truly won? Which scene is final? I mean, we've all seen *Zulu*.

Would Ellie's shock merge paths with adoration, her initial horror morphing into the opening chapter of a beautiful shared story that always makes people laugh when the couple embellishingly re-tell it? Or would her admittedly sudden departure come to represent a settled indifference to Alan or just 1990s mega-ballads in general?

For when time has got so late…
And no one noticed we were there,

We'll not settle for a dinner date,
When danger shows how much we care.

The singing was fitful, and even a few wayward harmonies started to slip in, a definite mark of growing confidence. Dave and Chris were doing this thing where they make a drum machine noise by slapping their cheeks whilst making an 'O' with their lips. It's supposed to be a bit like Queen; it's certainly endearing.

Someone ordered some more potato wedges as Will spread out the year planner on the barrel table.

'I can't say how proud I am of every one of you. We've had a great night, gents, no question. Alan's shown us all what's possible, with a beautiful dream, and an even better team. But there's a lot more to do. Right? Simon – can you spread out the Victorian sewer plans – the next one, I'm not going to lie to you, is a biggie…'

Home Time

With the printer's unresponsiveness now a glaring fact, popular television historian Professor David Starkey is, after much fiddling, realising that a USB port on his 14-month-old MacBook Pro might be broken. Some 57 miles away, in Hove, Zoë Ball has lost the run of a much-loved garlic press, lifted-slash-gifted from an early edition of *Celebrity Come Dine with Me*.

In Ashton-under-Lyne, Tommy Cannon cannot for the life of him remember which floor of the IKEA car park his S-Max sports activity vehicle is parked on. Worse, famous swimmer Duncan Goodhew has just trodden some Waitrose pretzels into the living-room carpet whilst momentarily distracted by his son's high-pitched laughter at a cable TV repeat of *The Sooty Show*.

On an otherwise balmy morning in Brooklyn Heights, Matthew Barney is all at sixes and sevens with an otherwise nifty Nest thermostat system, whose display is stuck on 88 degrees. Some 4 miles away, David Hyde Pierce has over-aggressively pierced the film lid on a tub of Dean & DeLuca creamed kale during a cast read-through of *Lost in Yonkers*, upending the contents over his artfully pre-scuffed Converse tennis shoes.

At precisely 2.29pm, as his car purrs up the driveway to the secluded cottage he bought shortly after wrapping on Michael Haneke's 2005 thriller *Hidden*, Daniel Auteuil is spitting tacks when he realises he's left Paris without his iPhone charger.

At home time, fuzzily defined as a nagging hour's-worth of minutes located somewhere between half-three and five, former

Defence Secretary Michael Fallon sits parked outside Camden Forest Academy for a good half-hour, listening to a terrible play on BBC Radio 4, before angrily recalling that he doesn't actually have any children.

In efforts pursuant to distant yet inflexible objectives, obedient to buried, unconscious drives and directives whose authorship remains unclear, the world stumbles on, its blood up and its guard down.

The Onset of Battle

'How long have we been here?'

Chris tugged Pete's sleeve as he asked, brushing a bit of mud off his left ankle. Pete continued to calmly stare through the binoculars as they lay, curled up under the violated topiary about 130 yards from the right-hand edge of Kenwood House. About 25 feet away the head and neck of a swan lay in the middle of the gravel path that led up to the house.

'Shh… keep your voice down,' hissed Pete, staring intently at the woods opposite. 'I think the second assault team have made it as far as the lake.'

'You mean Georgia, Jonathan and Katherine?' muttered Chris, needling.

Pete turned back to his partner.

'I mean… *the second assault team.* Try to stay focused, it's the only way to… to do well at this,' he finished. They continued to lie on the ground and their voices were replaced by the noise of insects loud and near, but also distant, less recognisable sounds.

Chris looked back at his boots and felt down his left trouser leg to the buttoned utility pocket. With luck this still contained some water and a cereal bar left from a recent walk on Sussex's considerably-less-dramatic-than-they-sound Fire Hills.

Pete shot him a look as Chris wrestled with the crinkly noise of the packaging.

'Right. I think we're safe to move out. Let's try to rejoin the armoured division,' – he gently unfolded an A4 inkjet-printed map – 'they should be at the assembly stage, just south of Thousand Pound Pond—'

'You mean beyond those trees?'

Pete's look was tired, parental and corrective, but he just nodded.

Chris jumped up.

'Great! Let's do this, *Mein Herr*! This bugger all has been going on for hours.'

✝

Seeing no one nearby, the stillness of the empty mansion only interrupted by muted tones of distant yelling, the men dashed forward in a series of diagonals, partial cover afforded by two damaged jeeps that had collided in front of the tea shop. The left side door of one was thrust up into the air at a broken angle; on it three words: 'Группа нападения четыре'.

They pulled up a little breathless by the toilet block before the path that had once led to tourist parking.

'We can't go straight down from here, too dangerous. We need to tack east, where there are more trees,' whispered Pete as they crouched by the entrance to Kenwood House's tea rooms.

'*Au contraire*, Peter. What we need,' said Chris, fixing on a point over Pete's shoulder, 'is an ice cream…'

A refreshment stand was lying overturned just beyond some picnic tables. 'Come on, we're out of sight. What do you want? Tub or cone?'

The sky was suddenly punctured at a single, fixed point. The flare detonated overhead, showering a pretty pink light over the building. It was only 7pm and still a balmy, sunny July evening. The additional light fell like an eye drinking in all it could briefly see.

'Amateur hour,' thought Pete. 'Wasting one of your three flares when we can all still see just fine.' Voices came from the spot they'd just left, near the car park. Friend or foe, it wasn't clear, but there wasn't time to worry about this point as their attention refocused on the deep clickety noise of tank treads approaching from the direction of the herb garden.

'Shit!'

They made a dash for the thicker part of forest that edged Kenwood's once well-kept parkland, just as the first detonation took out the pale Georgian edifice's right-most corner.

Some 12 to 15 seconds later the ringing in their ears had subsided enough to make out what had happened. Three tanks had pulled up around the house and a few remaining staff, mostly kitchen-based to judge by their outfits, were waving white tea towels attached to brooms and yelling in Russian.

'Fucking hell. How much were the tickets for this again?' Chris asked.

'A hundred and fifty quid, not including your outfit hire, I might add,' responded Pete, brushing off the soil that they'd ended up covered in.

'I mean, it's bloody good, isn't it!' Chris looked a lot more alive to the situation now. 'Thanks mate. Ledge-End...'

'Keep your head down,' said Pete and together they scrambled down the bank towards the farthest pond.

As they ran, the blend of adrenalin, noxious shell odour, and the effects of largely unfamiliar exercise began to foster a new sense of adventure. Its flavour was exciting. Normal life in a country that only engaged in remote, invisible nation-building had left these neural pathways unfired and unexplored. Comfortable jobs. Discomfort's ambit had been only social, familial or cultural. Was this grit? The 'real thing'?

Chris thought about screaming for a second. He really wanted to see just how loud he could be. Hear a man explode!

As they ran, Pete tried to contain his rising panic with vague recollections about ticket websites, hilarious reviews, insane price points, the hottest thing in town. 'Invasion – such a potent reconnector,' Mark Lawson had said. Plus you don't want to miss out on these things. It's the only point in staying in the financial war zone the city has become. Still, that sentence was easier to say when all the key words had been metaphors. Not like now, thought Pete, as he noticed the bullet-bent sign: 'Welcome to Hampstead Heath'.

'Isn't that Vicky Parks from MediaPlayers?'

'Shh! Where?'

Chris pointed up the slope to the broken low wooden fencing that edged a line of bushes. A young woman with brown bobbed hair was staring and prodding fiercely at her phone.

'Totally have a thing for her. Hot. In. Camo!'

'That's really not important right now,' whispered Pete, who was lying flat to the soil and staring at some other point to the west through his eyepiece. Chris stood up and waved. 'Vicks! Vicks!'

Pete pulled his ankles out from under him and Chris collapsed onto the grass.

'What the fuck are you doing? We don't know which side she's on!' he hissed.

Chris made gun shapes with his fingers.

'Aw come on! I'd happily be on her side, whoever she's shooting.'

'That is not. How. This. Works!' Pete whispered.

Vicky Parks turned to look towards them as another young woman emerged from under the bush, and together they seemed to confer for a second before unholstering their weapons.

'Yeah, yeah! I get it – stay in character, avoid capture, kill the baddies. Just saying. I mean it gets your blood up, this, doesn't it? Oh man, look, she's with Sarah Hills – also *hot*, oh—'

Chris stopped speaking as Sarah turned to face back into the treeline behind them before letting out a horrible guttural howl at the top of her voice. She fell forward, an arrow in the back of her right leg, moaning.

Vicky wheeled round and shot twice into the thick bushes above them, but the archer had already run. Pete grabbed Chris's arm. 'I told you, we've gotta go.'

'Where to, though?' asked Chris.

'Bowling club – it's hard cover.'

They dodged between the trees. What had always felt to Pete like the wildest patch of land in London now seemed horribly orderly, open and visible. As they darted forwards in short, controlled bursts of motion, deeply stored memories of childhood play guided them forward. Box Hill. The Devil's Punchbowl. Chaste banter with girls met on French campsites when the parents were getting drunk in the bar by the pool. Random access memories of when the unfamiliar had been easy to adopt and adapt to.

Virtual reality had failed on the launchpad just a Christmas before. A loss of sight was no way to see the future, just a new excuse to trip over coffee tables. Swatting CGI dragons in suburban homes had nothing on real-life promenade warfare. Once you'd done it (if you survived), it made total sense. Until you'd done it... it looked like madness.

The Siege of Gursk had been a fairly well-forgotten, slightly plodding WWII epic made in the mid-'60s, which presumably died a death when Oliver Reed and Lee Marvin turned it down (whether out of boredom or alcoholism). But as a plot line for a live theatrical battle experience it was super compelling. Star in big-production war film! No experience necessary! Plus, ticket sales had rocketed since the Russian annexation of Latvia. 'His dark materiels', as one waggish sub-editor had headlined it. It was the kind of publicity PR agencies kill for.

The sun had finally succumbed and a cold shadow had smothered the Heath. The trees seemed to become more dense with the light's retreat. Pete looked over at Chris, who had gone a bit 'method' in the last hour.

If a producer had been present, perhaps in a nearby dug-out, or watching remotely via tree-cam, they'd have smiled. Always happens. The personal transition required seems impossible until it is suddenly, utterly, complete. You just have to decide you're up for it. The distant muffled screams could be coming from high-definition speakers in the trees, or they could be the sound of real injuries. Evolution ensures you assume the worst. The uniforms help.

'Right. What's the plan? Take the bowling hut?' whispered Chris in the failing light.

Pete pulled out and unfolded a small piece of paper. 'No, we have to blow it up, it's going to be a distraction while Assault Group Two liberates the tennis courts.'

'Right. Let's fucking do this…' murmured Chris and the two men scrambled forward, full of renewed focus and adrenaline.

The producer was a cocky sort, but gave great interviews. It was an enthusing pitch. 'You know what you need? To taste the literal. Get your face out of that screen, scuff those knees again. Life begins when visual metaphors end.' What an insight that was. Remove the artistry and double-down on the intensity of the experience. So why not voting booths you could only reach by traversing a moat? Competitive parents' evenings conducted on climbing walls. Reckless acts of theatre. Comfort was weakness. Real imagination meant being able to become a person who does actually terrible things, for delimited amounts of time.

The Siege of Gursk. Why not? *The Rise of Man. The Great Unshackling.* A newly global Britain. *The Price is Death. The Heat is On. A Nation Votes 2: Vote Harder. A Spear For Your Thoughts. A Nation Fights.* Love me, scare me. Kill to get a ticket.

INDIANS ATTACKING FRONTIERSMEN.

Old Caziss

In Bar Raval, on an unassuming corner of a typical side street, is the original window bait himself. Old Caziss, the 71-year-old hombre with a thousand faces. A make-up technician of the highest artistry, he's the lonely face that's adorned three of the last six editions of *Lonely Planet Barcelona*. A theatrical everyman for all seasons, purveyor of analogue café theatrics nightly from table two, still keeping on in the era of glance, swipe, ignore.

At around nine o'clock, the June sun is starting to climb down behind the grimy red and orange apartment blocks that somehow gain grace as they lose detail. Off the square, couples are doing that effortlessly lovely-looking wandering, laughing, smoking thing. For the newly-minted-with-him-or-her surely a quick trip to the Raval? Let's go see what Old Caziss is up to tonight, *chica*? Maybe it's something good, something coo-coo, then a drink and a dance?

The window, elegantly inlaid with fading silvered deco patterns, has been his stage for as long as anyone can remember – which in the context of Barcelona bar life is around 17 to 20 years, give or take. People usually assume that it's his bar. Surely that's the only reason he gets to do that thing, whatever it is, every night? Or perhaps, as parents tell naughtier children, he lives in the sewers below, just coming up for a little money and a free sandwich.

Tonight's face is one for the broadsheet fans. Caziss appears from behind the bar and with a slight leftward nod to Maria who runs the joint, he takes the 1.4 steps required to inhabit the stage that is the final table on the left. His age is undefinable in that way of certain men who can't possibly ever have been young. Or maybe it's too many years applying a dense putty of foundation from six every night. Anyway, surely an actor of all professions should be able to stop time?

His make-up does the work of scenery. And drag scarcely does justice to the ensemble's ambition. One table, a window, the odd prop and a lot of intention. Grab their attention and a performance should work anywhere, was this small company's motto.

The crowd of tourists and regulars outside start laughing and clapping. For Caziss tonight has become Justice Beatriz Balzar, the judge busted only two days before for corruption in Bilbao. Luxury apartments, a Russian dancer, denials to priests and talk show hosts. The source material's almost too rich to bother with, yet here we are.

Caziss pauses to avoid tripping over his legal gown and grimaces dramatically, but are we the jury beyond or the defendants inert behind bulletproof glass?

His heavy jowls and rouged cheeks are nice caricature touches. Caziss's large hands pound the portable typewriter with a look of 'Who? Me?' angelicism (a deft jab at the dishonesties that fill Balzar's once best-selling memoir *Power and Precision: My Life at the Levers*). His hands stab and knead the keys like a conductor reduced to bread making. Then, with another imploring '*Culpables? Me?*', comes the climax, as two faux tear ducts taped to the sides of his face start to squirt tears at the window. The crowd goes wild.

It's one for the review pages tonight, for sure. Better even than the Clinton/Trump two-faces-at-once debate he staged back in July during the US election campaign.

The whooping subsides and Caziss stands effortfully before giving a full theatrical bow as Maria places his customary brandy at the end of the bar. Inside the sound is muted by the windows and the continued chat of the other patrons. The usual and dramatic usually converge in bars; this is how it should be.

And anyway, this is Caziss's home, he isn't the one who's gone out to be entertained.

The crowd dissipates rapidly, leaving two mid-thirties guys right by the window miming their adoration. Caziss looks at them with the practised eye of a stage actor who can read the reactions in rows one through ten without making any actual eye contact. Both guys are dressed as Anselmo, a character he played in the long-running *Amantes y Compañeros*. A grimace of recognition as he turns away, then. Every act is his, but he isn't any act. Brandy aloft, *gracias* Maria! Until tomorrow!

William Parsons in the Character of Don Lewis in the Fop's Fortune. From an Original Drawing by Parker in the Collection of Rich.d Bull Esq.r

The Gentleman Vanishes

It's usually during a lull in conversation that the inevitable question will show its plucky little face. The danger increases over time, and I hadn't seen a lot of this gang for months, not since Daniel's last birthday.

'So… are you *courting*, Andrew?'

Implicit smiley at the fun use of 'courting'. Comes up with uncharming regularity, but I usually just wince inwardly and absorb.

'Yes, of course.'

'Who is she? Will we approve?' More implicit funnies. I blame *Downton Abbey*.

'Well, I mean, I don't have a name to give you but the air is full of promise, things are definitely arcing in that… direction?' Slight pause while we both sip. 'I'll be married by Christmas.'

Bit overconfident that last bit, but the third glass of wine's a little booster whispering in your ear, isn't he?

'A Christmas wedding, Andrew! That's fantastic! Darling, Andrew's finally getting hitched!' Jeannie leans across from a parallel conversation and beams with a friendly, if sardonic, raise of her glass. 'Finally!'

'I feel I should be clear – there's no actual Victoria, Sally, Lynette or Rachel yet in the frame, per se. The same holds true for Conchitas, Emmanuelles and Janes. Katelyns and Imeldas also. But I think there just comes a time in a man's life when—'

'… You ought to take a wife?'

'Exactly. Although "take" makes it sound unduly Neeson-esque… But the will is definitely there, a lot of the groundwork, so to say, has been done. There's the house in Chiswick, of course—'

'A definite plus…'

'Right. And a whole load of fixes around prior issues, really solid. And you can amass so many key data points now, some of the graphs are quite revelatory. Likely wedding venues I've tabulated and evaluated. Possible locations for initial dates evaluated for their relative charm, offset against meteorological office data for the last 20 years and so on. The jigsaw is being completed, you might say.'

'Impressive stuff…'

'I mean, I don't want to jinx it and say, "Daniel, we have a foolproof system – join us", ha-ha! – no, that would be overstating it… But there are some Thursday nights when possibility just eddies about like an intoxicating mist. It's an exciting time.'

Daniel smiles, but is it you speaking or the person that you become once the words are spoken into the room?

'I mean, five years ago I probably hadn't even plotted the wine list variation matrix for Upper Street. Mad, really – I was really dawdling then, very second gear. As if a generalised presumption that an acceptable Pinot Noir could be had at a reasonable price point anywhere would actually fly in a live-fire situation on the ground. Bonkers!

'No, that's when it really hit me: you have to build up a detailed picture first. I mean, you're in business – you know how important robust data sets are, right? Detailed observations – get a sense of how the zephyrs voice their sighs across the borough, sunlight effectiveness quota south of the Essex Road across Qs two and three, which artisanal bakeries are really shifting units and so on.

'I'm taking the temperature these days, sensing movements in the air, but tasting only the telling pollen. Hence my confidence – but I'm going on and on!'

Daniel takes a breaded courgette stick from one of the host's daughters, who are playing serving girls for the night. A cool breeze flows in as a few people start dancing nostalgically on the patio to 'Common People' by Pulp, despite the dipping autumn temperature. Someone mentions William Shatner.

'Top up?' says Daniel, munching.

'Why not. Ah, the good stuff. She likes Pouilly too.'

'She?'

'She-who-will-be. Once it's all in the bag, as it were. Up and running. Personally, I can't wait.'

'She sounds special.'

'Adorable, really. We've somehow endeavoured at great length to have so much in common. But you know, if I've learned one thing, whether it's kismet's wings or centrally-planned-and-administered, love – it's just amazing, isn't it?

Daniel puts his plate down.

'Yes, absolutely – when I met Jeannie we—'

'It's that ineffable thing that underpins so much other information. Love. Amazing. I sometimes think it's this giddying gas that's gently gathering between the spreadsheets and the surveillance data. Did you know 24 per cent of women born after 1988 who currently rent in Tower Hamlets, Bow or Hackney have at least one band-related tattoo and use recreational drugs, but only at a purely recreational level? I mean, on one level that amount of detail seems, well, mad… But it builds up a picture, grades the senses to the actual, the possible. It's exciting, vital research. I'm 86 per cent more likely to remain in conversation with a girl called Amelia than a girl called Vista, Tamara or Jade. Facts, Daniel; hard facts build insight, alignment. Readiness.'

A glass hits the patio, topped off with a 'Fuck!', and the assembled crowd decides to recombine indoors. Sarah, whose home this is, strides across; 'Dustpan coming through!'

I turned back to Daniel, but he'd started chatting to a striking, dark-eyed young woman who must be called Harriet, Elizabeth, Lydia, Mariella; who must be a dramatist, a ballet dancer, a saver of souls south of the Mile End Road, a Portuguese teacher who turns out beautiful repro tables in beechwood, recently featured in *Monocle* magazine.

Matrices of possibility flip through a three-dimensional shape in my head, interpreting make-up choices as signals for potential outcomes. She glances over, not at me but at Christopher the performance poet, who's gripping his wine and lurking by the door. Poor guy, he doesn't look like he's really prepped for this.

ERIC, MONTAGUE, AND RUSSELL.

The Route

The advert had been teasingly, if probably inadvertently, enigmatic. 'Passengers needed for ongoing civic transport training programme. Paid position.'

A paid passenger? At worst it sounded like it could be dull. Days spent presumably circumnavigating the domestic wilderness here in zone 4 slash 5 at around 11mph. Ho hum.

But I had two months until a repeat surrender into academia would lure me north to Leeds and had been effervescing money in pubs like nobody's business. As if the flight north would be conducted on lottery wings. So much for that.

Then too a heartbeat-length fantasy of meeting some delightfully like-minded young thing similarly just-appointed, her life also on pause. *'We seem to share the same route…'* in the best clipped Cary Grant.

A moment's further reflection that 'passenger' doesn't have a verb form. 'Well, not yet,' I thought; 'you wait and see.' Maybe waiting and seeing would turn out to be key skills? As I say, the thing was all stasis and possibility. Envelope-stuffing was behind or possibly beneath me, I thought, and applied at once.

•

Six weeks into any job and you should be starting to get your feet under the table, they say. You've met the key people, figured out the nearest passable coffee shop and ordered your business cards. There's usually a slightly unnerving moment when you realise the new is the norm. 'Yes, Katie, yup. Yup. Exactly. We should have coffee. Next week?'

We're passing through the Meadway Estate, a gently

undulating grid of 1940s and '50s two-beds off the A316, its homes' tiny windows offset by gentrifying window boxes and occasional arty frills. As we drift by I can't help thinking that in just a few weeks I've become a regular 'one of the gang'.

This was one of my favourite parts of the route – a realistically uneventful section of about a half-mile long, conducted at around 4.45pm and on the border of zone 4. I felt like we started to really gel at Meadway. For one thing, you started to see an uptick in passengers and more variation in the overall taxonomy. 11am–4.30pm was the worst – just young mums and pushchairs, occasional school kids bunking off – most of it stuff the drivers could handle even without the magnificent preparation conferred on them by the Programme.

Andrew, today's driver, pulled us into a narrow space between an artlessly parked 4×4 outside an antiques shop and a seemingly abandoned red Hoppa bus. He snuck about 70 per cent of the bus into a space that said 50 per cent, tops. 'Impressive,' I caught myself thinking, starting to take this gig proper seriously. And it was true that after the initial bedding-in phase I'd noticed we were all getting deeper into the roles. As a 'parallel public' we weren't supposed to fraternise as such, all were to be as strangers, day in, day out. Maybe the solitariness helped deepen the delusion, for only then would we represent a test of the drivers' mettle. Mass transit observation demanded nothing less.

But we found little ways, people always do. I made a '7' with two fingers and winked across the aisle at 'Victoria', the 19-year-old who scribbles and chews her nails. I don't, of course, know that her name is Victoria, but it is clear that she chews (regularly) and scribbles (often) – which of these precise aspects were cast-iron parts of her original brief remained deliciously hard to establish. I like to think I can establish girls' names from small clothing choices through make-up gambits to possible literary achievements, finally ascending to the headiness of actual name likelihoods. Largely an untested area of armchair-detective work, sure. But then you have to be both actor and critic in this game.

'Victoria' smiled faintly back at my digital '7', then frowned back into her notepad and I resumed staring out the window at the fading afternoon suburbs. A '7' for a bit of finessed parking is all well and good, but you couldn't say Andrew had been fully tested – not yet. It was a Thursday afternoon, so the weekend was about to kick off – shortly Meadway and Twobridge would become Jäger-on-Thames, as the locals switched roles from retail management to beverage endurance analysts. Arise, rip-roaring regional deans of Alcoholica.

But mindful of my imminent return to the treadmill of organised education – seminars... note-taking... writing and marking... – I couldn't help but marvel at the Programme's didactic scope and ambition. Once graduated, these drivers would be trained to deal with anything the metropolis could throw at them. From bomb disposal to the pacification of escaped animals, the four volumes of the Programme represented a breathtaking matrix of readiness. I felt a little pride for a moment, playing my small part in the finessing of this fine metropolitan system.

The hydraulic doors exhaled and a lanky late teenager stepped on with a couple of associates in tow. 'Hello!' I thought. The last attempted to sneak in behind the second, head lowered as if his own attenuated view would confer invisibility. But Andrew was immediately on top of the situation:

'Oi – where's your Oyster?'

'I've paid, mate.'

'No you haven't.'

The trio sat down together in the seats reserved for those with an infographically heavy burden. It was a quality scene.

Perfectly executed, with the immaculate timing of veteran performers. At the back of the bus, 'Oliver', a 50-something in a moth-eaten tweed coat who was given to reading scripts under his breath, began to protest.

'Boys! You're holding everyone up. Pay up! Come on!'

That booming tone, such projection and reach – regional theatre? There were delicately credible tones of embarrassment, the mid-phrase self-doubting strangulation – a tincture of regret – it was all there. The boys remained all gangling wide-leg stance and confident staring. A mobile phone's tinny speaker started up a contemporary tune. *Chk chk pop trat! Chk chk aw right!*

Andrew hollered again from the cab, and in a move that surely marked a milestone in his advance through the Programme, performed a deft pre-drop combo: exit doors open, engine killed. Whammy!

'No Oyster, no bus, lads.'

The guns fell silent a moment and a pigeon wandered into view just beyond the doors. To break the silence, Andrew pulled out the big guns – and lowered the wheelchair access ramp, mockingly. Not PC, sure, but oh-so-very effective. The silence expanding within and cold air seeping in from the outside conspired to form a difficult weather front for the tough-guy trio, and with a final jumble of expletives at poor Oliver they slunk off the bus, slapping the doors and windows as they went. Bravo Andrew, bravo. There's an '8' or even a '9' waiting if you can keep this up through the suburb's lairy Friday night closing times.

Walkthrough

Okay, you're here with Chris – uh, 'RedTwo' I mean, ha! – and in this episode, well, a whole lot of shit's gonna get done, and get clear yo! So the new version has been out like two weeks now and I've been playing the hell out of this so I can share with you guys how to nail Level Six – which is a KILLAH! I'm telling you. It's doable but you're gonna need to bring your A-Games here, homies.

First of all, make sure you've already got the right outer layers for this one – the city is cold, man, just cold. So hit 'square' and make sure you've got the armoured three-piece with waistcoat, pretty rad I must say, but you're going to thank me, hahaha, in about, oooh, six minutes.

So where did we leave off? You've arrived just inside the town, fucking loving the detail in the drifting garbage got to say, real near to Big Eddie's restaurant and casino. Okay, so we're going to go up to the door, and the thing here is to take it slow, you don't want too much attention, not just yet *anyway*!

Right, we're inside, so scoot over to the bar, here you can order anything from like 20 different cocktails, and they all have different effects depending on the strength, so take it easy if you're new to this. Right, Moscow Mule, sorted – ten dollars, man! This city's gonna leave you poor – but you knew that, right? Hahaha. Okay now, feint left – there are three chicas by the jukebox, ignore the redhead – I tried that last night and basically she only speaks Portuguese, so unless you've got the European languages extension, welcome to a long, slow evening!

No, hit Up/Left and talk to the brunette, she's the target here. I like worked this room for four hours last night – till my mum got home hahaha! – and I can totally tell you this is Sarah and she's def the key to this level. The rose brooch on her lapel is pretty rad and you should totally mention it, hold Down and Left1 to make an opening comment about the brooch – this nailed it for me. Yo! And there she's smiling – we are IN *hombres*! *In*!

Okay, you can probably see there are now three other heavy dudes at the bar, don't pull the rifle or pistols out just yet, the trick is to act real cool – I know, goes against the grain, right? Now hit Action and Right2 – sweet! If Sarah's eyebrows are raised *and* she's smiling, this means it's all going to plan, so scooch over to the sofa.

Right – inventory check: do you have the book we stole from the depository on Level 5? In downtown? Good, you're gonna need it as while you're with Rebecca you can get 5,000 bonus points by mentioning you're well-read in poetry. Pull out the book with Action and Up. Nice work. See, both of your heads are closer together. Man, I wish it was this easy in real life, right? Hahaha.

Okay, now holding Down and Left1 is the bit they don't tell you at college – amaze! So you'll notice the lights have gone down – well that's just how it seems to you and her, it's like an effect of the talking or something. Now bring up the dialogue input field, oh-kay, and this is where it gets freaky good. Type the following, s'like a code but it's totally gonna unlock Level 7.

'Sarah, can I tell you about how I sometimes just walk into rooms and just catch you out of the corner of my eye, even when you're not there? And I'll think up a funny story, one in which I do not emerge too well (but not that badly either, it must be admitted), just to make you smile, knowing that though I can't quite see you, as you're not quite there, this would be what we'd do if we were just together.'

Wow! Like typing on this thing hurts, right? Damn! Okay, so now hit X and Down and bam! She's getting up.

Now the guys at the bar are checking out the room again — don't, repeat don't, pull the machine pistol as then it'll kick off and they'll totally have you. Okay gently pan 180, real cool like, and look she's got her coat and is waiting for you by the door. It worked! Amazing, you're on roller blades (ha! Joke! That's another level, *hombres!*)

And walk o-ver... yes. Yep! She flashed the smile. You're done. Bo-nus! Prouda you guys! We're still only nine hours in, but good job! Good job!

Things That Happen on Islands

Our first holiday
Discovered tomes
Beach-buried currency
Horse worship
Peacocks with remits
Cliffs and their cruel reputations
Coves with cove preferences
Cold sibling publishers
Some of the buildings turn out to be wooden stand-ins
Rock formations favoured by lovers
Harbours that harbour dangers
Noticeboard-mounted unequivocations
Incomprehensible gaudiness
Driving-side surprises
Auspicious tax arrangements
Impossibly elderly dowagers
Hyped ruins
Booze/pie recombinations
Professional postcard publishers
Picnic litigation
Childlike portions
Jagged rocks and rugged jackets
Coloured slate roofs that hide a sadness
Our last holiday

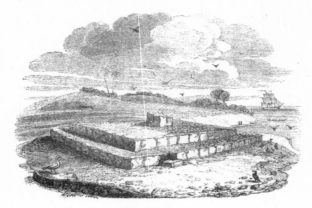

MALDEN'S ISLAND.

Year Zero

I'll be honest. One month in felt like an epic achievement. We'd all gather together, set aside our tasks for the day and try to share a sense of community. It helped dampen down the anxiety a little. I remember the toasts by candlelight fondly. But candles do unruly justice to the human face – anyone who tells you we all look better after dark is a fool.

Jacqueline had a kind of practised pout, and a can-do earnestness that had earned her a few advantages when we were assembling the initial shelters. She's a strong presence in the group. I like Jacqueline, we get on. But I feel sure she'd point the tigers in my direction if it came to it. Her hair's definitely held up better than most. I wonder what she's found to put in it?

The campfire had begun to spark and roar. It was always an optimistic sight and the warmth was welcome too, given the island's exposed aspect and the increasing lack of trees.

Georg looked good too, his face inclined as he listened to Jacqueline's latest poem about the sunset, a rich theme she would return to time and again. An engineer by former calling, Georg tended to look restless and impatient during the daylight hours, but then we must have made for poor labourers. Once lit by flames, though, he took on an explorer's poise, his face jutting forward, seemingly ready to reach for greater goals.

Twelve of us, sitting together eating and drinking, it was almost a civilisation restored. Blur your eyes (and your memory) a little and perhaps you might imagine we were at a festival, one of those upscale ones where there's a suckling pig and the millennials dress like Red Indians. That's not the PC term, but then that stuff doesn't come up so much any more.

'Year Zero!' Jules held his plastic cup aloft and smiles broke like waves, soundtracked by the actual sea about 300 yards away. 'Year Zero!' we followed, in a discord of enthusiasms.

With a Jules on board, a group will thrive. Be honest, 'indefatigable' is a word you rarely hope to use about people in day-to-day life. But when you find someone in your midst who genuinely deserves the term, and with your back against various still-to-be-assembled walls, points should be awarded.

Jules was the second son of a former war correspondent, somehow battle-hardened despite a childhood in the Cotswolds. Rugged, charismatic, I want to say... leaderly? And bearing a smile that builds confidence in the least talented or most upset is a valuable and powerful skill. We all love Jules, in our different ways.

•

It must have been about six or seven weeks after the final camera guys went missing. It had been a tough old time. We'd destroyed the last of the saws cutting down the dragon trees to build the visitor centre. Someone said they'd evolved over 20 million years. They certainly proved more than a match for the prop-quality tools that the TV company had originally brought with us to the island. Crappy tools whose disappointing qualities were intended to cause predictable upset and outbreaks of blame-storming between 'characters'. It was a grim realisation when it dawned on us that dragon trees take some actual slaying.

But then you have to keep revising your plans. Adapt, adopt, extend your lifespan. So we all live in the 'visitor centre' now, it being the best built of the completed shelters. And references to the television crew have subsided. It's rather as if we've always been here, just as we've become.

In any *tabula rasa*-type situation, you're hoping for a nice mix of skills and a breadth of personalities. The nightmare scenario would be, say, all insurance convention attendees, creative writing retreaters, or the touring cast of *Miss Saigon*. In that respect, at least, we had lucked in.

Predictably (although I didn't predict it, not even slightly), once we'd got some semblance of a roof over our heads (and buried Sally and Nathaniel), attention turned to bigger questions. It was Alannah, our recovering American as she put it, who first suggested that perhaps we should write a constitution.

In my English way I'd internally bristled at this idea, largely out of cowardice at the battles I feared it foretold. But after it came up again around the campfire one night I started to see possibilities, openings.

Despite the liberations of life on a deserted island, rules are the first thing you crave after food and water. Realisations are sharp ended or bitten-in, almost always dangerous. In a tiny place all manner of norm violations become possible, admissible. And in the unknowableness of an island 146 hours by boat from the nearest mainland, every rule must be forged afresh. We became squinters, looking for advantage. Just as your long-distance vision gains acuity in hopefulness, you think bigger about immediate social questions. Maybe it was prudent to get stuff down on paper after all.

Obviously there are a few big hitters in the constitution world, names to be reckoned with. But as a group, we wanted to go our own way. New stresses and emphases. These days I remember 'freedom' mostly as the realisation you'd wandered into the wrong movie screening. But in this situation you become more... how can I put it? Prescriptive.

That morning we'd all assembled in the clearing where the helicopter had crashed back at the end of the times-before. Edged by thick foliage and on a slight promontory, it had become known as 'Breeze Top'. The broken rotor blades that thrust up out of the sand added a sort of dystopian call-back to things we would only revisit inwardly. Plucky rescue attempts. Summer blockbusters. Will Smith.

Breeze Top was our religious totem, our dignity in adversity, providing a small sense of historical mastery over nature. I joked to Jacqueline that perhaps one day they'll erect a gift shop where you can buy printed copies of our founding documents. She failed to laugh. But I'm getting ahead of myself.

The insects were at their most insistent that week, so proclamations would be punctured by the sound of cursing and slapped flesh, but that had probably also been true back in that other time, that other country. All eyes and ears were facing forward. Fittingly, it was Hark, the day of listening, which comes after Rea, the day of rest.

The general idea had been for everyone to take a bit of time to go off and come up with ideas for our new governance structure, then bring them back to the group. Exciting times. It's not often you get to be in on the ground floor of a civilisation. A chance to be a Washington. A Jefferson. Who was the guy that ran New York? Oh yes. A Bezos.

Although the sun was blazing, I spotted Jules, a silhouette moving by the tree line. He seemed to be reciting to himself, no doubt preparing his contribution. He moved his palms upwards, outstretched in an expansive gesture; perhaps he intended a spiritual focus for our founding documents? That gave me pause, but Jules was always all positives, so I just smiled and walked on.

Cross-legged on a broken plastic palette at the other side of the clearing were Eleanor and Paul, deep in discussion. They'd bonded early over previous careers in political social media, and the way Eleanor held Paul's hand as she spoke showed a deepening bond. In another time and place it would have been an unremarkable scene, enacted in a thousand public parks every summer. But I ground my teeth. We needed to legislate as individuals if we were to make rules fit for a group, not a group of dualities. I'd been hoping everyone could rise above their own narrow interests, on this of all days.

An hour or so later, as the sun's intensity started to weaken, Georg blew the emergency whistle that regularly summoned us all to Breeze Top. Alannah joined him, a pile of sun-blanched leaves in one hand. She hadn't been long out of university when this change of scene had befallen her. Some joked that she'd become Georg's intern, unpaid but keen to learn, picking up some of the island admin that filled more and more of every day.

I could just about make out a few words scrawled on the top leaf, probably using charcoal from last night's fire. So this was it. Our visions recorded, now to be shared. The end of the beginning, but would this lead to the beginning of the end?

•

Georg began to speak, awkward and faltering at first, but Jules, who was standing by him, stepped forward and laid a brotherly hand on his shoulder. 'Let's all pay attention to Georg – he's worked hard to bring all our ideas together. I can't wait to hear them and I bet you can't too!'

Jules beamed, his face its own little sun as Georg began again, this time a little louder.

I looked around. Mostly rapt attention. Thirty or so people who'd unwittingly found themselves founders, agnostics in charge of a creation myth. There was excitement in those faces, but also a kind of weary horror. A sense that the appearance of formal rules might bring change in status for some.

Jacqueline was wearing the red sash that she washes clean for important occasions, but as she approached her smile was tight, her face unreadable.

Georg began to read from the submission finalists.

As I'd feared, the first few proclamations were more rites than rights. True, you can't spend six months searching for food and sleeping under the stars without becoming thankful for the basics. So yes, now we pledge a kind of allegiance to the sun – I wasn't going to lose any sleep over that. Plus a lot of people did yoga first thing anyway, it might if anything make mornings a bit more social. One down.

The next four suggestions were on their surface about the preparation of food – well, the killing of things that might or might not constitute food. This was firmer terrain. Always good to know what's up for grabs... and what isn't. Boundaries.

Next, a couple of obligatory bits of score-settling dressed up as turbo-charged etiquette for a brave new society. Could it really exercise one of our number so greatly that what passed for soup was swallowed mouth-open? I'd always followed the Asian logic that you took in more oxygen. But then a small island necessarily connives at quibbles.

And then there it was. The gear shifter. The promised premise. The moment we knew we'd broken new ground and perhaps left behind our past selves forever. Instead of murmured assents and mumbled exceptions, just... silence. A moment of shared realisation and beauty.

Perhaps in a way it actually was 'self-evident' that we would eventually have to go to war. After all, no one had ever really dealt with the particularly modern variant of PTSD that being abandoned in the middle of a television pilot really represented. We'd focused on staying alive at first, no shame in that. But in our new founding, we found that there was an animating anger after all.

" ' WILL YOU KNOW WHAT WAS IN HIS HEART?' CRIES HE" (p. 85).

Because eventually your expectations shift in nature and scale. You go from expecting to be rescued to wanting to learn about hut design. You stop obsessing about mortgage payments on the flat in Worcester Park and get anxious about whether you're bringing in enough fish with that sorry excuse of a spear you fashioned. Not: 'When will the boats come?' but 'Surely coconut milk can be fermented?'

As Georg continued with his toneless recitation, I felt stronger than ever. This was right. We *would* form a standing defence force. We would regard off-comers as secondary. We had the right to arm bears. (There are no bears, but this was a great joke from Paul; we all shared a conspiratorial smile.) They'd left us here for sport, taken our once considered lives and discarded them. But together, we'd found a nature that was stronger than theirs. We had been militant in our creativity, our resourcefulness, but you can't live in metaphors when your very survival is at stake.

The wind whipped up and we huddled a little closer. I noticed a few held hands. Lovely. I liked this new direction, I have to say. And Jules as King? Fine. It's not like anyone lives forever. You need structure, authority and, yes, charisma. When the others came, as eventually they surely would, we would be ready.

Week Two

The towpath on the Regent's Canal between Camden Town and Stratford offers the newbie cyclist a tempting alternative to the angry *mêlée* that fills London's roads. You usually have to spot the entrance, then negotiate a short obstacle course of railings or gravel or cobbles down to the level just below ground. An escape, of sorts.

The government-subsidised bike-to-work scheme, mysteriously still operating in an era of gung-ho austerity, was made much of in your 'Week 1 Welcome Pack'. Turns out a pretty capable two-wheeler is yours for about 250 quid. Thank you to the mandarins down the hall who've somehow not nixed that one, and I'll take the black roadster with the quick-release wheels. Very nice.

First weeks are always a bit overwhelming. Open-minded attempts to soak up roles, rooms and rubrics whilst not falling into the trap of befriending the wrong members of the hierarchy. After such a week you'd normally nip to one of the decent boozers near the Old Vic or across to Borough and catch up with friends, but this isn't that kind of job. You've been assailed by downloads and datasets, appraised of regional dangers, up-to-speeded on evolving threats.

Still, it's week two and there's a call from the loading-bay guy: your new bike has arrived. And so three, hours-long, full-immersion meetings duly completed, you descend in the secure lift to the concrete bay to meet your company wheels. An anonymous black bike for an anonymous new career. Its lightness is pleasing as you wobble out onto Vauxhall Bridge in the sunset. The speed is another unexpected, but then you are the youngest of the new intake, so let's be at 'em.

Twenty-five minutes later and you've crossed the water north through the shabby quiet of Pimlico and somehow navigated the Brownian motion of Oxford Street. You cross round the back of King's Cross, making a right by the headquarters of the nemesis newspaper and lower yourself onto the towpath.

The water's stillness seems to add to the quiet as you pedal along, and although the light is weakening behind you, the warmth of the ride gathers as you propel yourself along the towpath. It's six-something as you pass the fashionable lights and sounds of Broadway Market, the food- and book-stall owners now disappeared below decks.

In the gathering gloom, it occurs to you that your new bike's lights are a bit unimpressive, and a couple of times you've realised you're not as noticeable as some of the professionals. Still, early days. And quite a workout, this. You're getting a little heavy-legged as you take another narrow under-bridge turn and spy the start of the now closed Victoria Park to the left. The air is clean but your head is full, after six hours watching detailed presentations about former satellite states, republics gone awry, overlays of oil movements, docked fleets and changing boundaries.

You've slowed to a gentler pace and the chill of the evening is more pronounced. Summer isn't here yet, that's for sure. Where does the urban heat dome end anyway, zone 2? You hear the distant rattle of a bike frame that's just hit the cobbles, at some speed. No bell, though. Someone's keen to get home too.

The social housing styles that line the canal accelerate through the '50s, '60s, '70s and '80s as you power along. Differing takes on what to do with people, balconies replacing gardens, Juliet gates stapled to third-floor windows, but then no one has children any more, not at these prices. Some lights are on, but despite the jumble of styles, community seems to have taken the night off.

The towpath's a little less maintained this far along, and the paved bit narrows. You manage a backwards look over your right shoulder for the split second that this is possible when travelling just 2 feet from water. It could be a combination of the temperature and the light, but for a second you have the impression that the cyclist behind you is moving at a speed for which the adjective 'interceptive' might be coined. Alone, yet racing. From? To?

You push up from pootle to purposeful. There's that form of thought where the surely ridiculous and the tangibly certain coexist. Good old fear of the dark. And then there's your new career, with its emphasis on a professional pre-emption in the face of regrettable possibilities. Insights mean incisions. Maybe you're just being thorough, as per bullet points 2 through 17 yesterday, but you start pedalling like billy-o.

Approaching the uplift at the edge of the park, the towpath forks – straight on takes you down to Canary Wharf, left is a switchback that hugs the east side of the park and drops you back near Old Ford. It'll be fine, it'll be fine, as up the cobbled hill we climb. A stop and a breath, slowed by the barriers, but it's quiet enough to hear. To hear a bike also turning right and down onto this side of the canal.

Your colder blood says let's get zoomy and fifth gear-y and how it's only a short trip home from here. Ricocheting around your head: will it be like this every week and is this what a really significant career change actually feels like? Privy to privileged information; always basically 'on'?

As you pass another identical sandy-bricked housing development, you risk another look back over your shoulder. A mistake, a surging panic up both sides of your neck. A terror occasioned by the fact that even in low temperatures, London's style-conscious cyclists don't normally don balaclavas.

The front light of the pursuing bike is eye-like, focused and bright in this, the darkest stretch of the towpath. You decide to focus by blotting out, and hitting play on your phone brings up something randomly pumping. But then it would be awful to spend your last moments in an attempt to soundtrack your own exit. *Bourne* versus *Born to Run*?

Nearly, now, nearly, now, whirring feet that power round. As you barrel along towards Hertford Lock you manage to widen the gap a little. Just long enough to evaluate possible scenarios. You're supposed to be a good interpreter, a scene-reader, an opportunity-spotter. Are complex, guilt-ridden fears a side effect of highly irregular exercise? Or is this, in fact, 'a practical'? Part of the induction programme? What must be understood, analysed and acted upon? What, in short, must you be prepared to 'get done'?

The training slides were clear. Actions steeled by the grim-faced adoption of the passive voice. 'A response was actioned by the engaged units.' 'Steps were taken pursuant to standard protocol.' 'Cover was afforded by the bridge's supports, during the unit's armed response.'

Too flowery. Imagine the press release and work backwards. No, it's only week two.

'Establish three facts about the suspect, wordlessly.' That was fun on a pub-based training jolly, all that let's-use-Sherlock-as-a-verb cold-reading stuff. But now your fact-free fear is real, if powered only by the circumstantial, the animal.

'Analyse, recognise, neutralise,' the growing awareness that for all the high-power devices you've been issued with, that real intelligence isn't reducible to words on screens. It's something bodily and partial, a rapid build-up of facts that stimulate action or overwhelm.

Fifth gear starts to feel too heavy. Worse, those bike-traffic-calming metal barriers ahead are going to collapse the tensed space between you.

Who's got your back, as it were? The real higher-ups never put their names on the organogram. 'For fuck's sake tidy up, Harris!' Assuming that still is your name. 'Housekeeping – end of a job, and make it quiet, would you?' Give precedence to form and procedure, in everything. Last acts hopefully imbued with some minor poetic indication. 'The civil servant is thought to have disappeared beneath the waters that were once the city's industrial livelihood.'

You're a bloody company man now. Make no mistake, this is a role for the ambitious, but everyone knows they're plausibly deniable at all times – it's the dark matter holding the whole thing together. The remote kill switch glows in a drawer disguised as a different drawer, somewhere in the doorless room at head office. But I don't yet know anything... All that stuff about the launch sites in disputed border territories? You'd watched that on Russia Today's YouTube channel, *eff eff ess*.

'Your back light's off!' breathes the eye-rider as he zips by, a motive mass of middle age, ziplocked within Lycra.

The solid emptiness arrives in his wake, a block of air dark and forceful. You exhale, imagining the graceful aerial pull-out of a mapping application on a tiny touchscreen, peered at in the half-light of a forest somewhere near a border crossing. A blue dot, a tiny potential, a heat signature, precise coordinates with imprecise motivations. Stay on it, we want updates. It could almost be someone heading home.

Stagecraft

The room was a bright white, with the composed atmosphere of an art gallery. My shoes made an imperious tapping sound on the polished wooden floor. High above, subtly recessed lighting bathed everything in an unshowy luminance. It was the full experience, one had to admit.

The body-length box dominated the middle of the room, but it was only when you got up close that its human scale really became obvious. It was what, 20 steps from the gallery's opening to the plinth it sat on? It prepared the visitor.

I walked towards it, a keening sense of excitement building as I stepped forward on the polished wooden floor. This was absolutely going to work.

Standing alongside it, the workmanship was clear. Thank you, Morrell Art Productions SW14; never a duff job, those guys. A mahogany frame holding four lightly tinted reinforced glass sides, with a wooden base inlaid with memory foam. Plenty of room for one's arms, and a spare 6 inches either side with raised squares for the display of key objects. Lovely. Two beautifully drilled and finished holes in the top glass panel for that all-important oxygen, ensuring this was not, contrary to initial estimations, a coffin.

'All good?' hollered Alan from Morrell, appearing in the entrance.

'It's amazing,' I replied, giving him a wave.

We stood together looking at it.

'Reckon you'll be alright in there?' he asked, passing me the bag of decorative and storytelling items for the case.

'Oh yes,' I said, all eagerness and enthusiasm. 'Well, thanks to you I shall!'

As we stared at the box a little inward giggle scrambled up the back of my throat. The very thought of it. And even then this was only one part of a much, much grander strategy. This day was already a good day.

On Tuesday morning, there was a knock at around 10. Majid the postman smiled as I opened the door.

'Morning… Big one to sign for…'

And so it was. I scribbled onto the screen with one hand as I took hold of the 4-foot-long tube, like grasping an awkward dog. Even in this digital era, architects seem still wedded to the drama of printing things out on massive sheets of paper. Perhaps it helps justify the costs, which had similarly scaled ambitions. But I didn't mind. There's something exciting about rolling out 2 square metres of paper plans on the dining-room table, weighing down the corners with glass ashtrays. The game is afoot and all that.

It took a few minutes to fathom how to read the plans, even with the centre-light blaring down. There was a key to the symbols in the corner, but I'm new to all this really. Eventually I twigged. Once you found the high street at the bottom, it all made – I want to say, 'sense'?

My first foray into the property game, this, and nothing so dull as some forgettable one-bedroom flat in a borough no one's ever heard of. Oh no. The coffee shop had closed down with three months left on the lease, so I'd nabbed it for a song, which freed up some cash for the architectural adjustments that would make the plan work. It must still resemble a coffee shop, of course, otherwise people wouldn't come in. But the alterations

I'd brainstormed with Storm and his team were an absolute kid's book of delights.

The front of the coffee shop would work just as before. Let them come. Gaggia machine, pastries, moderately ludicrous descriptions of bean flavours scribbled on a blackboard. Tick, tick, tick. But then as one walks farther into the seating area to the rear, things get a lot more interesting…

The ceiling will gradient from the original dull beige to a painted *trompe l'oeil* resembling nothing less than a late August sunset over Jaipur. Birdsong will gradually be discerned from recessed speakers. Actual birds are also encouraged to frolic, entering the space via a nut-and-pipe system that connects to the rear. (Seen you and raised you, Owl Café.) The tile flooring gives way to fake grass and box hedging as the punter, muffin and enormocino in hand, wanders back in search of seating and succour. The transition is deliberately provocative. 'Are we inside or out?' ask the coffee-curious. 'This café makes me nervous,' a woman in her early thirties will say. 'Why are there no seats? And why is there a man hanging in the sky holding a bunch of flowers, Mummy?' Ah, the questing minds of innocent children, always straight to the heart of the matter.

Your questions are salient and timely, young scamps. For 'tis I, in the harness in which I hang, made of fabric coloured to appear invisible against the 'sky', in which I hang for four to six hours daily, wearing a pale blue suit, holding a bunch of flowers, feet 2 inches above the floor, one foot forward, as if I've stepped out of the sky. I'm told it's terribly affecting. I toyed with calling it 'Love From Above' but that felt too on the nose, so 'The Limitless Potential for Encounter With One's True Object of Desire' it is. Long titles show you're serious.

But back to all the doing that must first be done! The build phase commences on Thursday and, all being well, the scene painters will begin the sky fresco in early February. I have to tell you, I can't wait.

A smudgy orangey six-by-four photo sits above my fridge, a relic of when photos were seldom and papery. Ten children are sat at a long table covered in coloured card, industriously crayoning under the watchful eye of their teacher.

'It's not what you paint, it's how you *look* that makes you an artist.' That's what Miss Rogers, our art teacher, had said. I loved her, of course, without knowing what that meant yet, feeling it instinctively. The interest she took in our class was so honest and delightful. She had the carefree charm of the funny people we watched in sitcoms while we waited for our hair to dry before bedtime. I might have been only 10 years old, but I somehow knew she had provided us an adult truth more far-reaching than any of the stern policies our own parents had thus far shared.

We did our best work for Miss Rogers, each of us hoping to win her affections with works that brought innovations of all kinds to the staid world of paints, felt-tips and crepe paper. She didn't know it, but she was a legislator: she'd made the rules, with a careless mussing of our hair in reward for paintings variously ambitious, garish and tacky. Our destinies were chosen, our audiences set.

I gazed over at the two lads who were knocking out part of the front wall of the flat. I'd always hated the gloominess of my little basement digs. I felt instinctively that Miss Rogers would approve of these alterations and preparations. Soon everyone would be able to look anew, see afresh. And, dare I say, learn?

My upstairs neighbour, Roger, had voiced concerns about the structural effects, but I'd put him at ease. No dug-out oligarch's disco dungeon, this! And the architects had assured everyone that replacing the front of the apartment with reinforced glass would add value to the whole block. I assured them it was modernism and upgrades, dialling down the performance-art dimension. Let those dice fall where they may, but on another day. Who knows how many will actually care to linger and drink in the view of this, the world's very first 'Romantopticon'? Surely better not to create anxieties about merely potential threats at this stage. I gave the two busy workers a cheery wave and made a facial expression of hearty goodwill and common purpose.

Wednesday morning was all London plain, unending grey sheets pulled firmly down like blinds. I had just emerged from the tube at Old Street roundabout. The station, despite years of surrounding gentrification, remained a reminder of the car era's bury-the-pedestrians principle, all grim tunnels and dank walkways.

But grey's a great background for colour, I find, and 10 minutes' brisk walk east and the old mood had lifted as I approached the cool canalside office that was my destination.

The thing about digital stuff is, you've got to be a revolutionary. There's simply no point creating your own version of the Jammie Dodger or the custard cream. Your new e-morsel must redefine the very contours and topography of biscuitdom.

This all-or-nothing quality was something I found terribly appealing. After all, what was my own project if not a my-way-is-the-entire-highway attempt to reset what a sloth-like culture called 'romance'? The team at Unthk embodied the anything-goes peppy get-go I thrive on, so I knew we'd be on to a winner with the app part of the equation.

Existing body-toning photo apps are strictly for your entry-level developers. Sure, you can project an ideal, gloss up your hair and thin that paunch, but I had something more... comprehensive in mind.

The algorithm Edward and team have come up with is nothing if not merciless in its commitment to creativity. Its ambitions for me are as high as those that I would hope for from myself. Higher, if anything. Samuel, the fresh-faced developer leading my highly agile team, handed me a bundle of print-outs.

'Print-outs! How analogue!' and I softly punched his upper arm.

'Yeah! Still, you're gonna want to see it all laid out, I reckon...' and he started to arrange the A4 sheets out on the four old school desks that formed the office's main communal workspace. The logic was simple yet overwhelming, imperious yet almost unbearable. One app, yet millions of profiles to choose from, all of them somehow me. One of those ideas where success is the moment someone yells at a pub table, 'Why hasn't anyone thought of this before?' Well, quite.

Together we reviewed the algorithm's first flush of creativity:

#	Name	Height	Salary	Location	Hair	Fun Fact	Picture Props
1	Ralph Peat	168.6	£22k	Keswick	Brown	Freckles	Tank helmet
2	Jez Bump	172.4	£40k	Chiswick	Blond	Coke habit	Coldplay wristband
3	Gary Partling	169.5	£150k	NYC	Mousey	Doesn't know own middle name	'Blessed emoji' t-shirt
4	Alan Framp	157.8	£N/A	Hove	Toupee	Can limbo	Complicated briefcase
5	Chris Tools	182.0	£250k	Antibes	Bald	Still buys CDs	Leatherman tool
6	Clive Watson	165	£50k	Ipswich	Loose perm	LARPing	Inflatable sword
7	Terry Sparks	190.4	£29k	Glossop	Side-parting	Antiques fetish	Pictured in armour

The app had really got into the swing over the weekend, probing every nook and cranny of human variability, its hound-like nose truffling for the good stuff.

I confess, in just a few minutes, in their wildly different ways, I'd fallen in love with them all. What a pageant of manhood! Such a palette of gentlemanly possibilities, each with my face reimagined with every tolerable twist of genetic and social status. Once we hit a million variations (Wednesday around 8.47pm, if progress continued at the current clip), this thing would be ready for the world. But would the world, for its part, be ready for this #AllofMe era?

You can always see farther, so keep looking – that's the mantra. Together, by detailed plans and programmed actions, we can divine and define the chemistry of our intentions. That sounds a bit perfume ad, sure, but I'm paraphrasing from that historian's TED talk. Ultimate awareness born of mathematical certainty and sheer hard work.

These efforts aren't gimmicks. Many people make that mistake, don't beat yourself up about it. I've just found a way to live in the present. That may sound obvious, but it isn't. Most people are either 10 minutes behind the now, or stuck in the foreshadow of hopes based on where two further decades might take them. For all the artistry (and computational expense) involved, my approach keeps me absolutely bang up to date. No true artist cares about 'legacy' – your gift is to be in the present moment. Simply, I am all of me.

Sometimes my head aches for days. I call it the pain of plans, the weight of wonder(ing). On these occasions, I will retreat to the sofa bed in the lounge, farthest from the noise of the street, to recuperate. Absolutely no caffeine, head steady under duck-down pillow, a light duvet, and lie inert until it all passes. (I keep a notebook and pencil under the coffee table, but I've never had an idea worthy of the name in this state.)

To be alive is to be alert to everything everyone else might have missed, to be sure. And though I (we) detest the time lost to reverie, there's always the delicious possibility that the avenues of the mind that we wander down in slumber might take us somewhere new.

I will see you everywhere. You will see me everywhere. We will smile and everything about us worth caring about will be registered, swallowed and understood. For we are becoming inevitable, you and I. As I write these words, even with the gathering heat at the temples, I both know this to be true and almost unbearable. What wonder awaits.

Availability

I walk into many unfamiliar buildings. Double glass doors at street level, a bored out-of-hours security guard, a book into which I will scribble my name though neither of us can foresee a situation in which this information will be referred to. These unremarkable buildings often bear names that are poorly thought-out stabs at grandiosity. Regal House. The Summit Building. Temerity Tower. Okay, I made that one up, but you get the idea.

It's a walk-on part, of course. And you don't need a lot of training to pencil your name in the book and find the lifts – they're located with an insistent regularity, perhaps to prepare you for the many other consistent features of the modern office job. As an outsider on the inside I've developed the ability to look at home among any combination of rounded-edge ersatz modernist office furniture. You walk at a confident speed directly forwards, letting your peripheral vision establish your relative position to the kitchen, toilets, meeting rooms and, worse-case scenario, 'ideas lounge'. There's a point where nonchalance and indifference meet in the middle of the graph – that's the bit to aim for.

The magazines on the coffee table vary depending on the building's prevailing inhabitants. Nobody picks up magazines any more, of course, but I find them interesting, a little window into the local customs, wisdoms, the royalty and the rotters of this or that particular community. Cover star Margaret has encouraged 30 co-workers to plant a garden on the roof of her company's headquarters. Her smile is appealing, but she looks a little distant. I wonder if her own flat has a garden?

Soon a door opens and we gather to begin. The facilitator

is rummaging among his notes. It's not very convincing, but part of the drama in which we must all play our regular roles. The paper is already scribbled on with crossings through or completely blank. But they all do this, you see. While you sit around a table trying to simultaneously suss out the other participants' level of knowledge, ambient sanity and potential threat to your own largely imaginary credentials, the session convener will feign interest in something on the desk. A laptop will be toyed with, head dipped, to ensure there are just a few seconds or even a minute in which to establish the required state of nature in the room, some sort of level playing field between the leader and the led. 'I have gathered you all here this evening...'

It's always more or less the same, despite the subject at hand and the intentional randomness of the participants. During the pre-task we have already self-identified using tick boxes, averred interests in 'x' and 'y', given assurances that our bona fides are intact with regard to wage, occupation, star sign and past experience. Now, it is show time.

The city has many economies. Daily sales of products, clothing, food, are the obvious ones, of course, captured in pored-over charts of demand and supply that are usually presented as a fair picture of the nation's beating pulse.

Then there are the under-table traders, contra-legal professionals and vice-sourcers. But in a way these are just as obvious and necessary, darker but just as timeless functions of the city's emotional matrix. For to make Friday night ultra-peppy, please to dial Jules, Zeppo, 'Freddie', 'H'.

But somehow more obscured are we labourers of the edges. We're performing strange, shifting, transactional roles. Ones that underpin long-nurtured dreams and ambitions for which the city is both booster and detractor, fertiliser and desert. Leaflet distributor. Call-centre occupant. Out-of-work actor/

in-work historical torture re-enactor. And then, of course, there's market research.

This, my new world, seems entirely populated by mittel people, usually in mid-life, available mid-week. We're valued for our education and professionalism, yet somehow motivated by small envelopes containing untaxable denominations, grounded and established, yet able to mobilise trending opinions at a moment's notice.

I started doing it when the session guitar gigs came to an abrupt halt after three years of drinking away the goodwill of some nice people who were actually paying alright, now I look back on it. I like to think of it as a return to school drama productions. I tend to don the suit I got for Spider's wedding – a costume always adds to the performance. Maybe I'm not quite a gumshoe, but in case pop music comes back begging, I thought it might be worth using a nom de plume, and thus 'Harry Banks' was born. A bit stolid, but all solid.

I get a call from Eleanor, which I'm pretty sure is her real name, to establish a few basics, even though we both know that I'm yessing-up to propositions that can't possibly be true because we agreed to their counterfactuals only last week. Purchasing and procurement experience – check. Familiarity with barrel lengths – yup. Grasp of kill percentages and destruction dynamics in built-up areas – sure thing. It never seems to affect my eligibility on the day, though, so that's pretty sweet.

I didn't finish my degree, but I did read a lot in tour buses as we trundled slowly across the matrix of Welcome Breaks that define a musician's England. There's time to talk around subjects and you soak up radio phone-ins, the tiny details that drive local news, the passingly solved problem of other minds.

Also – total winner this – the previous tenant of my little shared flat in Archway never cancelled his subscription to *The*

Journal of Project Management, so I flip through that for notes on mood and style. It's a perfect, specification-free, lorem ipsum job – no one, but no one, ever asks for details once you've uttered the words 'I'm a project manager.' Bingo!

I got started with the small stuff. I mean, it's dead easy to have opinions about Nespresso coffee makers, LCD TVs or an energy company's iffy use of a lovable penguin in an ad campaign. 'Bring it on!' I thought. Two hours of opinioneering (okay, I made that up) for sixty pounds in a brown envelope, plus it gets you out of the house; you're meeting people, all those things that are supposed to be good for you.

And sometimes we're not just opinion providers; we become a kind of jury. A disparate rag-tag bunch who've been convened to save the world from some really awful ideas. There was the small group of guys who had to assess four potential 'creative routes' for a male-targeted mint breath spray called 'Ice Me'. That one got ugly. Or the time myself, a child psychologist called Esther and a novelist called Steve ganged up to destroy five separate adverts for 'Addy', an energy-bill-obsessed, deal-lovin' animated elephant who's always lookin' out for you. You're welcome, world! (Somehow the salad bar chain Tossed was green-lit in the teeth of our delectably well-articulated objections. You can't win them all.)

You could call me (Harry) the opinioniser, the thoughterator, the insightifier. I find I read a lot more these days too. Sometimes I download demo software to get a feel for the professional life, and I now use an online diary to 'time manage'; it all adds to the quality of the performance and the texture of the feedback.

My double Harry is a bit of an overachiever, though I admit I've a soft spot for him. The beautiful Chinese girlfriend Jin-Li does something impressive for IBM in Beijing and they're both about to invest in some rather nice property in east London.

And Harry's had some great jobs, especially when you consider that he's only 36. That's kind of the perfect age to be in a city like London. You've long built on educated foundations, you've been around, travelled, had fun with night people and started to think a little longer-term. At 36 you can meet the eyes of a 52-year-old future you, whilst still delivering just-credible opinions on the latest fads to the twenny-summn' brigade. Your consumption patterns form powerful stories that people will pay for. Thirty-six, I'm telling you, just stick with that.

Toby, the facilitator of tonight's session, finally looks up from behind his laptop with a bright smile, the fiddling complete. 'Ah, got to love PowerPoint, right!' and all eyes are frontward as the 48-inch screen on the far wall suddenly displays a picture of a missile aimed up at about 45 degrees in front of a pretty sunset.

'Right – let's just go round the table – first impressions? Chris?'

Chris, who is probably late forties, greying and could plausibly hail from almost any type of public-sector management role, furrows his brow a little.

'Ukraine, Putin's summer '14 campaign?'

There are a few controlled titters and Toby smiles broadly as we all continue to stare at the image on the screen, considering our ways into the topic.

'Ha! Yes, not bad, not bad at all. I think this was actually shot near the Kazakh-Russian border, but good call. Any other first impressions? Clare, what do you feel about it?'

Clare is spectacled, reserved seeming, dressed in the mute tones of above-basic-price-range Zara, and grips her biro tightly as she responds.

'I… I think it's initially impressive, you'd expect a definite morale boost for the operatives nearby, in the field, they'd respond positively to this…'

'That's interesting… Anyone else with an initial reaction? Oh sorry, I meant to put the name up too.' Toby clicks the presentation and some wording flies in dramatically from both sides of the presentation, written in what I instantly spot to be a little in-joke: Impact font.

Terraviza Corp. M246X CRADDA
Ground-to-Air missile system

I decide to jump in.

'It looks like the rear launch mounting has been pared back to the absolute minimum – that's got to mean great fuel efficiency in a large-scale battlefield context.' Thank you *Jane's Defence Weekly*'s occasional series of email explainer videos (and the cable channel where history is weaponry coming to life).

'That's great, Harry – so you're drawn to weapon systems that represent a good long-term ROI, yes?'

'Absolutely, I think it's only responsible procurement – you can't just look at how many city blocks a system can render to ash, after all, and in modern warfare there are so many other competing demands to budget for, it's got to fit into the overall mix…'

Nice opening salvo – good, solid stuff. That's probably all I need to say for the next ten minutes. Emily, who's sat near Tom (who I happen to know was a reasonably respected painter in the late '80s until all the YBA stuff upended the market for his take on airbrushed irony), shoots me a slightly worried look. It's possible I've forced up the performance requirements a little early. It's a deft dance, but then the somewhat chunky £150 fee for this session is really rather impressive; was I wrong to prepare a little more than usual?

Toby has produced some large foam board advert mock-ups from under the desk and is holding one up, reading aloud:

'Right let's look at some ad copy… "The M246X CRADDA ground-to-air missile system features new Sky-Claw technology, climbing to 1,000 feet in under 2 seconds."' Toby radiates resolute neutrality, his manner brimming with the neatly ordered sequentialism that one would presumably need in order to use the pictured weaponry itself. 'Does that resonate with you, Tom?'

Tom and I have crossed paths twice earlier this year. A round-table discussion about some ill-fated triangular biscuits, and a mindshare session on the future of the Liberal Democrats. He can be good, but he's a little wayward on occasion in what's always an exercise in meeting expectations, however circuitously.

There's a pregnant pause, and then Tom breathes out thoughtfully.

'I think I'd need to be able to visualise the intended target more literally before the speed would be a killer factor, actually.' The room tilts its head, chewing down on this observation, which takes two to three seconds to solidify as insightful rather than just something, anything, to say.

'I think an image of what it's really capable of destroying is a sort of prerequisite for its speed becoming super-compelling,' and Tom ends with a flourish, 'I wouldn't want to feel I'd bought something that was all sonic boom and no boom-boom.' It's peerless stuff, and I'm high-fiving him inwardly as I maintain Harry's professional serious face, as this is, of course, a matter in deadly earnest.

One mock-up follows another. We opine, we tap our fingers, the hive mind's actorly congress in full session. Somehow, madly, everybody present is getting their money's worth. The wrap-up is positive, and some great ideas, really, have been shared – and thanks.

·

We've come quite far out to sea these last few months, Harry and I. My mind seems so ready to encompass and improvise. I'm tuned to parallel truisms, voicing personal opinions rapidly and unconsciously crowdsourced from the zeitgeist. Chancy riffs weaponised with inner certainty. It's one long back-to-back solo for us two; just give me the key.

Perhaps this is what those personal development people are talking about the whole time – you know, pushing your boundaries, taking on new challenges? And maybe Harry will marry Jin-Li – they seem so well suited, those two.

I'm omnidirectional and I like it. Features are not fixed at this time. We can optimise, front-load and beef-up later. It's more the overall vibe I want you to understand and react to. Two hours well spent, I'd say. Who knows what we'll think tomorrow.

Managing Expectations

The day we turned it on? God, that'll remain long in the memory. Of the survivors at least. Countless changes, great and small.

It's ushered in something of a new era of discovery, too – in fact, our aim had always been focused on solving one big question... and now? Now all the little things we took for granted seem to contain this new, previously unseen physical property: 'quantum peril'. The location of towns, the weight of water, the possibility of heights, each a little bit broken. It's heartbreaking really.

In retrospect, the research was both amazingly detailed, rigorous and compelling, and yet also breathtakingly narrow. We probably need a new word for that. It might help to place the whole episode in context for future generations. Assuming there are future generations.

Problem is, you stop seeing some of these theoretical nuances when the equipment gets beyond a certain physical size. People get invested in it, the wiring, the colourful ducts, the sheer amount of lasers. I vaguely recall we gave some of them names early on: Henry, Cressida, Alonzo and so on, you know, to gin up some public enthusiasm during the build phase. It was a different time.

We turned it on at exactly 12.12 GMT+2 on 12 December 2012. Clive Maddings, engineering co-lead, had confided in me that this was a physicists' in-joke about atomic densities' behaviour under conditions of near-unknowable pressure. One of those cutely cocky gestures that typically only gets noticed in the *New Scientist*'s diary column, and possibly a few of the geekier podcasts. It was low on my list of must-disseminates, certainly. Yet somehow this attempt to stick the fundamental building blocks of reality into a long-running maths in-joke came to frame, understandably sourly, the public's response to the whole affair. Everything from 'Twelve Reasons Why Science Can't Be Trusted' to the more bombastic 'Hang the Boffins!', which made dispiritingly regular appearances in the tabloids.

Of course, I'm not blaming the public. Anger born of loss is understandable. Particularly in the immediate aftermath, once it had become clear we'd lost some of the prettiest parts of Switzerland. Those are now what the experts term 'Z-space' – dimly comprehensible to humanity as not-really-height, yet somehow ineffably more horrible to deal with than not-width-or-mass.

You told yourself, well, that area wasn't that densely populated, hillside agriculture was becoming financially untenable anyway... But the nagging sense of guilt was still there, casting peak-like shadows.

(By the way, the Esperanto word for 'sorry' is *'bedaŭras'*. We all did a course. It sounds better, doesn't it? One pictures a homely cottage, its windows illuminated by candlelight.)

The button itself isn't really the issue. People do love to ask, though. And yes, one of them was red, as it turns out. I suppose that's an understandable mis-expectation. Blame Hollywood.

No, in reality it's a series of levers connected to a massive array of switches routed together by virtual cables that exist in a fluctuating power matrix that runs out of the complex and into the... mechanism above. I won't bore you with the ins and outs – it hardly seems important given where we are now – but yes, of the four master controls one was red, as it happens.

I just thank God that when the original press release went out, to announce that we were... going to turn it on, that we really had all our ducks in a row. I mean, back then there were people who couldn't see the value in getting bound copies to give out in the room or having the risk assessment professionally typeset. But I told them, 'No one on this team is going to undermine 27 years of literally weapons-grade scientific endeavour and a budget that could run a medium-size Balkan nation, for the sake of a poorly chosen typeface.'

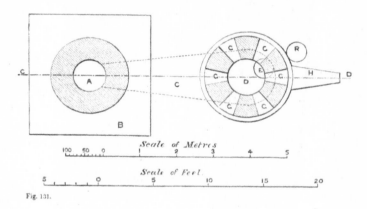

Fig. 131.

You have to see a macro-scale scientific endeavour like this in the round. Yes, a lot of it involves advanced mathematics and the precise alignment of lasers more powerful than the sun, deep within the bowels of a concrete building in a place we used to call Bern, but I've always maintained science is really about storytelling. Advanced maths, high-power lasers and storytelling. If you haven't got all three, pulling together, you really don't have 'a thing'.

It was a hard sell at the Institute but we eventually got the funding, and the budget was there, no question. Educate, elevate, oxygenate. 'But must we not also demonstrate mastery of the science of communication?' I would often ask at the start of meetings. It feels like an empty flourish now.

Creatively, the agency's concept to have those

underprivileged schoolchildren from Chamonix turn it on, was... possibly a symptom of an idea that had got a bit out of hand. Overconfident, I mean overconfident. It got out of hand about 16 minutes later.

But yes, perhaps the team probably should have spent those final few hours rerunning the risk algorithms rather than helping out on a video for that, at the time adorable, song they'd written... about the machine.

Of course, it's a little too early to say whether the fact that most of the people in the control room, *die Kinder* included, became a new kind of gelatinous gas only visible in the octaprismic register is actually a bad outcome, per se. I mean they could be having the time of their lives. I'm assured we won't know until we complete the next round of experiments.

Sadly, those are a way off at the moment, as most of the publicly identifiable scientists have been hunted down for now. That's those that weren't immediately thrown into the howling six-dimensional portal that opened up between Avignon and, well – somewhere 'else' is our current working assumption. These days a little humility when making large claims comes with what's left of the territory.

Me? I guess like so many things on this once beautiful planet, I've found I've had to pivot to a new position. But if a professional marketing qualification is about anything it's about finding new ways to cast old, or as in this case, perpetually recent, problems.

So let's reflect on what we learned the day we turned it on, say I. I'm often called on to provide leadership for those coming up, the recent graduates, the marketing newbies, or even those who've literally and unnervingly just winked into existence. I have my stump speech ready. It's from the same one I used at the trial.

'What makes us who we are isn't the towns we build, the

symphonies we write, or even the number of dimensions we can readily comprehend without horror. No, what makes us truly us is our ability to translate. Maths into energy, English into German, danger into opportunity, love into understanding. Translators have to create new worlds and we're creatives, every damn one of us. And guess what? That's what's going to get us through the next unquantifiably shaped yet somehow reassuringly horrifying combo of bent time and tentacular verticality that we used to call 'the future'. The best ideas? They're not from above. Everything thing we need is right here in this room. Love you guys; now let's get out there and share the good news.'

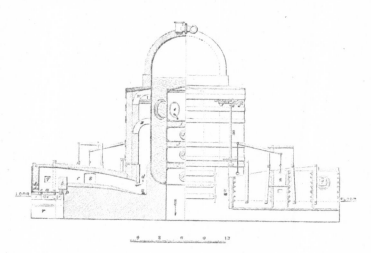

Words to Songs from the Album Also Called *Not From Above!*

Liner notes:

Those identified as morally culpable for this confection would, I assure you, be mortified to think of you reading (and re-reading) the following lines as poetry. They are lyrics, words to songs, musings for melodies, nothing more. In fact, they're probably best read only under referential circumstances of lyrical confusion – and in that way we can, of course, excuse you while you kiss this guy.

1. Not From...

Not from... *a leaflet from the seminary*
Not from... *a hope for the extraordinary*
Not from... *documents imaginary*
Not from... *any hope that we would marry*

Not from... *wisdom partly planetary*
Not from... *overconfident vocabulary*
Not from... *an order from the military*
Not from... *the fear of being solitary*

2. On Peacock Island

When we first hit the sea,
Down on the beach there's an island in reach, where
We could play kings and queens,
If only for moments rowing our dream boat,
So come give your hand to me,
I promised a fable from the toppest of tables,
Just over this tiny sea,
Our fortunes reborn before the break of the dawn

And if you should, care to follow,
I will promise, an end to sorrow...

> *We'll share our ambition, to a regal rhythm*
> *– on Peacock Island*
> *They'll herald our mission and our dazzling decisions*
> *– on Peacock Island*

When I first caught your eye,
The display was all feathers, a heart yet untethered,
When you first caught my eye,
I knew in a moment, desire's atonement

So help me drag, this boat to save us,
We'll steal away, don't call the papers...

> *We'll share our ambition, to a regal rhythm*
> *– on Peacock Island*
> *They'll herald our mission and our dazzling decisions*
> *– on Peacock Island*
> *We're refining and honing, this Game of Enthroning*
> *– on Peacock Island*

The triumph is brewing, in our modern ruin
– on Peacock Island

This island's too big for one, don't tell me that you're leaving, Princess
Together is how we'll become, history's master and mistress...
... on Peacock Island[1]

1. Peacock Island or 'Pfaueninsel' lies in the river Havel in Berlin, with a 'love castle' built by Friedrich II for his mistress Wilhelmine Enke. True to the torrid, the castle burned down, but they've built wooden film-set style replacements, which doesn't have to be a metaphor.

3. The Greats

I was all set, all to forget, the things love does to you
Who did I think I was kidding?
I read the greats, from morn 'til late, drinking deep from wisdom's brew
So who was that, set my heart spinning?

> *But what do I know? I'm just the guy who*
> *Took a tumble underneath your poetry*
> *And when I see you, that blessed shape who*
> *Stirs my thoughts anew to curiosity*

I ducked the sting, that deadly thing, with equations deep and dark
Just, for once, could I be colder?
I wrestled with, the endless if, how to live without a heart
Truth be told, with a lack of candour

> *But what do I know? I'm just the guy who*
> *Took a tumble underneath your poetry*
> *And when I see you, that blessed shape who*
> *Stirs my thoughts anew to curiosity*

> *And when you see me, so deeply reading,*
> *It'll be your letters not that book I bought*
> *The motivation? This new sensation,*
> *Written there in chapters two to four*

If 2+2 was never 4 baby... and the sun sets in the east you say
The theory's good but not too good to question,
My silence means there's just too much to say...

Repeat choruses

4. Deleted Scenes

I can still recall the feeling, when the cameras start to roll
A forward-with-the-madness keening, anything is possible
Two thoughts later on the trapeze, I'm not sure what brought us here
If the stunt man phones in poorly, shouldn't we begin to care?

> *... Shout! ... Cut! I don't think so*
> *Cashed! Out! I don't want to*
> *Deleted dreams – all that's left when we're through*

They won't use all that they heard, some of it absurd, or just too softly spoken
They won't have kept all that we did,
the scenes in which we hid, lacking Oscar motion...

> *... Shout! ... Cut! I don't think so*
> *Cashed! Out! I don't want to –*
> *Expleted themes left behind on the floor*
> *Shout! ... Cut! I don't think so...*
> *Cashed! Out! I don't want to*
> *Deleted dreams – all that's left when we're through*

See I told you for real in the back of a bar, but we were too drunk to remember... The twist at the end of the film was the bit when they pan back and show you she never... I know how this ends...

The message I sent might as well have been lost from the moment the movie had started... They cut to the chase where my grand monologue was supposed to have left your heart melted... I know, how this ends...

... Shout! ... Cut! I don't think so
Cashed! Out! I don't want to
Deleted dreams – all that's left when we're through

5. Your Hot Friend

On the morning of the first day
The scene was bright if not exactly gay
We were amazed you'd made it through this,
Galaxies exploding in that kiss…
But when do you know… does it lie like driven snow?
'Yes…' you said, but 'No…' you meant…

> *Your! Hot! Friend! A face like victory*
> *Your! Hot! Friend! A shape made history*
> *Your! Hot! Friend! A way with symmetry*
> *Your! Hot! Friend! Has got the moves*

On the morning of the third day
Upper management began to fray
Our people out there getting restless
The latest thing was causing some distress
For the graphs do clearly show, something new begun to glow…
'Oh…' you fear… 'Don't forget – that I'm here…'

> *Your! Hot! Friend! A face like victory*
> *Your! Hot! Friend! A shape made history*
> *Your! Hot! Friend! A way with symmetry*
> *Your! Hot! Friend! Has got the moves*

Once we felt all that we did was cool…
Passing notes on those rumours heard after school
Look up at night and the stars will spell out who
But beware the voice that calls from just out of view…

Repeat chorus

6. First Impressionists

When I think of all we've done and how the scene is drawn
I couldn't do this all alone, so where did you come from?

We were going blank and it was only morning
Not exactly sad... but the colour's a little boring
Did you think that I would actually remember
The things we said that morning in July?
But what do you know, now that we glow,
The picture's as clear as the sky...

> *The first impression that we get*
> *The closer you are, no, no not quite yet...*
> *The first impressions are never set*
> *But blurring your eyes, defocus and then...*

We were on the brink, and it was only dawning
Not the bed you'd think, but wishing and hoping...
Our tonic, something fake for all the sadness,
Your weakness for coincidence was cool
Could it be a new religion or just madness?
But I was hoping to become your happy fool

> *The first impression that we get*
> *The closer you are, no, no not quite yet...*
> *The first impressions are never set*
> *But blurring your eyes, defocus and then...*

When I think of everything we've done, and how the scene is drawn
We can't do anything all alone, so where did you come from?

7. New Zounds

These are the new zounds,[2] bright multicolours,
Better than others that you might have seen,
Theirs is a new sound, skittles that knock down,
Dazzling dance crown, now this crowd can dream

New zounds... yeah!

So these are the new zounds, proud exclamations,
Decidedly spacious in their heads' repartee,
But I noticed your get-go, from the moment the first note,
Moved us to dancing, this ballet for free

You must wander, inside wonder, if to muster, something good
Don't try harder, it's no bother, to be all you should

The accent's not right, but just for tonight,
We'll bathe in their light, and make it our own...
The sounds kinda grating, but you don't leave love waiting...
We dance here persuaded, by the lights of the town

New zounds... yeah!

You must wander, inside wonder, if to muster, something good
Don't try harder, it's no bother, to be all you should
You must wander, inside wonder, if to muster, something good
Don't try harder, it's no bother, to be all you should

---

2. 'Zounds' – an archaic term expressing surprise or indignation:
'"Zounds!" cried the Admiral, "the picnic is quite overcome by bees!"'

8. Should We Fix It Together?

A single thought through the smoke so black
I wonder if we could still turn back—?
Promise hung in the air like a lonely feather...
As our eyes met across the wiring frayed
The nearest town's 10 miles away
Tell me do you think, should we fix it together?

> *For when they write, what our history becomes*
> *Mistakes take their place at the centre*
> *Ignore those instructions and manuals of course*
> *A twist and a shake make it better*

We were only s'posed to stay the weekend
But now marooned you're my only friend
Potential filled the air like descending weather
Is it love at last or just a shame decayed?
Into my mind the truth sashayed
Your smile the tool to a mind somewhat detethered

> *For when they come, with the plaque circled blue*
> *People think first of the theory*
> *But knowledge so practical and right on cue*
> *Is the stuff you remember as victory*
>
> *Should... we... fix... it... together...?*
> *It... could... work... forever... yeah!*

A single thought, a consuming wish
Could we tie together this thing we've stitched,
Thrown together on the road to somewhere better?

9. Loyalty

I will be loyal to this campaign for a beautiful terrorism
I'm so spoilt, you picked me, the keenest face in the queue
Your bidding, so cruel, yet endlessly fascinating
Then emblazoned, in sunshine, the badges with your face anew
Count me on your inner team, to bring about this awful dream...

> *Loyalty, to the Queen, to your beauty and all between*
> *Liberty, so seldom seen, dead to me, it's just a dream*

I'll be your foil, in the battle to establish your endless rule
Commitment is total, we're chattels, like the posters said we should
But no turmoil, will rattle, the folks when bang on queue
This Spring's new fashion, is action, our hearts no longer made of wood
Count me on your inner team, to bring about this awful dream...

> *Loyalty, to the Queen, to your beauty and all between*
> *Liberty, so seldom seen, dead to me, it's just a dream*

'We will mock your victory, all praise endless beauty
Standing here to obey, thoughts we cannot convey...'

> *Loyalty, to the Queen, to your beauty and all between*
> *Liberty, so seldom seen, dead to me, it's just a dream*
> *Loyalty, to the Queen, to your beauty and all between*
> *Liberty, so seldom seen, dead to me, it's just a dream*[3]

---

3. 'Loyalty', it would be fair to say, is a pretty awkward title for a song, but there are #reasons. It was written for an exhibition by the excellent Greek artist Stefanos Rokos and 'Loyalty' was a musical reimagining of his painting, *Loyal to the Campaign for a Beautiful Terrorism*. Reproduced with kind permission, facing page.

10. At The Double

On an afternoon in May… a fear you couldn't quite allay,
Should you post that letter by the door?
Why does it take so many words to state,
Something people use their eyes to say,
With a smile and nothing more…

Words don't come that easily but
Were there a job opportunity,
The moon and stars in unity,
I'd be yours at the double.
Should head office have an opening,
For a motivated starter who's angling,
For a chance to take you cycling,
I'd be yours, no trouble.

> *If there were a chance you see… to tell you what you mean to me*
> *Well sometimes the words get lost at sea, mumbled or sung so quietly*

So the form's filled out in triplicate,
The font's award-winning and the colour's good,
My referee says you really should,
So I'd be yours at the double…
If the museum needs a new dinosaur,
In a notice pinned to the kitchen door,
In that position I'd yell for sure,
'I'd be yours!' at the double

> *If there were a chance you see… to tell you what you mean to me*
> *Well sometimes the words get lost at sea, mumbled or sung so quietly*

'I'd be yours!' at the double
'I'd be yours!' no trouble

11. Three Kings

I'm sure you knew, that summer was in retreat now,
Rebuttoned anew, wistful of view but thinking of
The way that love needs, the breeze for its optimism,
Kicking up leaves, just out of reach, those chances missing

> *Three kings, while you slept were travelling*
> *Ten miles, in an ageing tiny car*
> *These days, suitors aren't a mystery*
> *You think, replacin' make-up on the tray*
> *Three dreams, of loving in the winter time*
> *One theme, 'Take me far away from here'*
> *For once, avoiding baubles on the tree*
> *To find, something lasts eternally*

I'm sure you saw, that postcard that hit the doormat
Handwritten means, stamped for a dream... distracted by—
The radio's on, could that snap in the air be your heartbeat?
Sleigh bells all wrong, but those Christmas songs
Always leave you smiling

> *Three kings, while you slept were travelling*
> *Ten miles, in an ageing tiny car*
> *These days, suitors aren't a mystery*
> *You think, replacin' make-up on the tray*
> *Three dreams, of loving in the winter time*
> *One theme, 'Take me far away from here'*
> *For once, avoiding baubles on the tree*
> *To find, something lasts eternally*

12. Not From Above

Not from above!
It's become rather clear just as we'd all feared right at the start
That light in the sky's not enough, but the face we saw, was yours
True, the rumours compelled, but the newspapers sold us a pup
At the top of the hills it was cold, and that henge an unspeaking clock

Pious words can get mumbled (and)
True... the story's always taller than trees
True... we only wanted something to believe in
If truth is beauty, be someone we can see...

Not from above!
Couldn't see near or far, the ravine claimed our car, but we looked
'Cos we'd heard that your name was a star, to be gazed and loved upon
Well, no tablets of stone were on sale at the summit's gift shop
But our mission was suddenly clear, your name would reign from here

Not from... a leaflet from the seminary
Not from... a hope for the extraordinary
Not from... documents imaginary
Not from... any thought that we would marry
Not from... wisdom partly planetary
Not from... overconfident vocabulary
Not from... an order from the military
Not from... the fear of being solitary

Not from above!
Felt as sure as we had about anything we'd ever done
And your face in the dark was the light, a sight as bright as the sun...
The terror was firmer when love was the thunder we felt
And that thought was a smile, a word, and by firelight we melt...

Pious words can get mumbled (and)
True... the story's always taller than trees
True... we only wanted something to believe in
If truth is beauty, be someone we can see...
True... biased hearts often stumble
'Cos the truth is somewhat harder to read
And true, I only wanted someone to believe in
So if truth is beauty be someone we can see...

Not from above...
Not from above...
Not from above...

Credits

All songs by Alexander Mayor
Produced by Myles Clarke and Jonathan Hucks at Grand Cru,
London, in 2017

Alexander Mayor ~ singing, guitars, bass, programming
Mike Monaghan ~ drums and percussion, trumpets
Joe Thompson ~ piano on 'First Impressionists', 'Should We Fix
It Together', 'At the Double' and 'Not From Above'
James Hill ~ double bass
Clare Younis ~ backing vocals
Samantha Whates ~ backing vocals
Amy May ~ violins and arranging on 'Peacock Island'
Garo Nahoulakian ~ guitar solo on 'Your Hot Friend'
Members of Chaps Choir ~ singing on 'Not From... Above'
Chris Bailey ~ additional drum mixing

Thanks…

Alexander's Festival Hall has always been less 'a band' and more
a reasonably sized venue in which to assemble an ever-
changing troupe of the lovely and talented. And so sincerest
thanks are due to all the above players and the following top
people for brilliance in countless instrumental ways:

Mike Smith, Joe Smith, Simon Hughes, William Mayor, Dominic Stichbury, Alice Mayor, Angela 'Piney Gir' Penhaligon, Samantha Whates, Thomas Venker, Sarah Szczesny, Chris Thow, Robert Mesure, Stefanos Rokos, Julius Beltrame, Travis Elborough, some of the many voices of Chaps Choir, and my parents Ann and Peter Mayor for moral support, much encouragement and some lovely stringed instruments.

www.alexandersfestivalhall.org

Unbound is the world's first crowdfunding publisher, established in 2011.

We believe that wonderful things can happen when you clear a path for people who share a passion. That's why we've built a platform that brings together readers and authors to crowdfund books they believe in – and give fresh ideas that don't fit the traditional mould the chance they deserve.

This book is in your hands because readers made it possible. Everyone who pledged their support is listed at the front of the book and below. Join them by visiting unbound.com and supporting a book today.

Richard Allen
Felix Andrew
Danielle Antonellis
Caroline Archer
Michael Archer
Seb Baird
Tomas Baltazari
Mary Beacham
Louisa Beckford
Fiona Bevan
Julie Biron
Donna Blackburn
Alec Bowman
Luke Bowyer
Hope Calnan
Toby Calnan
Sara Cannon
Leo Chadburn
Tim Chen-Hudson
Tracy Cheung

Stuart Clark
Josienne Clarke
Richard Clews
Mark E Cooper
Fiona Cousins
Sarah Cronin
Dwane
Dickon Edwards
Chris Evans
Jens Friebe
Daisy Froud
Dave Fuller
Hannah Gatt
Katrin Geilhausen
Ann-Marie Gilkes
Piney Gir
Jonathan Griffin
Juliet Gutch
Elliot Harris
Tom Hilverkus

Hannah Hughes
Laurie Innes
Diana Jarvis
Ben Johnson
Tim Johnston
Michael Jones
Dawn Kershaw
Miia Koponen
Paul Lawrence
Luke Marlowe
Nick Massey
Bill Mayor
Iona McNeil
Susie Mesure
Laila Meyrick
Gemma Mira Jones
Huse Monfaradi
Carlo Navato
Alice Nicholl
Molly Nielsen
Janet Oakes
Jon Palmer
Nick Parker
Sally Perry

Rebecca Poole
Cony Poole
Danielle Regan
Adrian Richards
Jesse Richards
Susan Roberts
Jim Roebuck
Leesa Rumley
Sophie Ryden
David Sanchez
Kathryn Smith
Mike Smith
Michelle Soto-Teall
Jim Stichbury
Simon Storey
Ivan Teage
Georgina Terry
Stephen Troussé
Eoin Tuairisg
Russ Welch
Heather Willensky
Bobby Williams
Jeremy Worman
Tamsin Worrad-Andrews